SEAMANSHIP NOTES

Angus Ferguson

Lecturer Glasgow College of Nautical Studies

WITHERBY Seamanship
INTERNATIONAL

Witherby Seamanship International
A Division of Witherby Publishing Group Ltd

4 Dunlop Square, Livingston, Edinburgh, EH54 8SB, Scotland, UK

Tel No: +44(0)1506 463 227 - Fax No: +44(0)1506 468 999
Email: info@emailws.com - Web: www.witherbyseamanship.com

First published 2004
Reprinted 2006
Reprinted 2008
Reprinted 2010
Reprinted 2012
Reprinted 2014
Reprinted 2015
Issue 6

ISBN 0-9534379-6-5

Printed and bound in Great Britain by Charlesworth Press, Wakefield

Published by

Witherby Publishing Group Ltd
4 Dunlop Square, Livingston,
Edinburgh, EH54 8SB,
Scotland, UK

Tel No: +44(0)1506 463 227
Fax No: +44(0)1506 468 999

Email: info@emailws.com
Web: www.witherbys.com

Contents

Navigation

1

Voyage Planning

Appraisal

From consulting all relevant publications the potential dangers on the voyage are identified. After considering existing routeing schemes, environmental factors, reporting systems and vessel traffic services a clear indication of a safe route can be obtained.

Planning

Tracks can be laid on the chart from berth to berth indicating the pre-determined margins of error. Danger areas are marked on the chart, as are points, which could be useful to navigation. In the event of an emergency contingency plans are also considered. The plan is approved by the Master prior to sailing and must be kept onboard the vessel for 12 months.

Execution

Once the departure time is known the estimated time of arrival at the destination can be found. ETA's at critical points in the plan can also be determined. Times of high water and a clearer indication can be gained of the conditions the vessel is likely to face throughout the voyage.

Monitoring

The vessels progress is continually checked against the planned route. Any necessary deviations are amended in the plan and the bridge management team advised. The navigational equipment is monitored and checked on passage and prior to departure.

References:
Safety of Navigation Annex 24 – Voyage Planning (SOLAS V5)
Safety of Navigation Annex 25 – Guidelines for Voyage Planning (SOLAS V5)
STCW 95 – Chapter 8
Bridge Procedures Guide

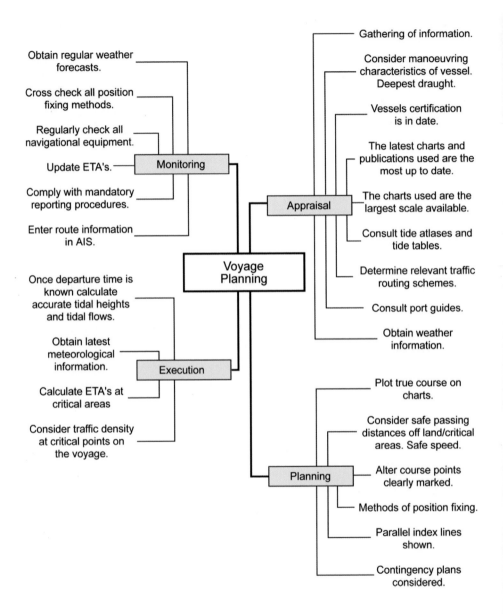

Obtain regular weather forecasts.

Cross check all position fixing methods.

Regularly check all navigational equipment.

Update ETA's.

Comply with mandatory reporting procedures.

Enter route information in AIS.

Monitoring

Once departure time is known calculate accurate tidal heights and tidal flows.

Obtain latest meteorological information.

Calculate ETA's at critical areas

Consider traffic density at critical points on the voyage.

Execution

Voyage Planning

Gathering of information.

Consider manoeuvring characteristics of vessel. Deepest draught.

Vessels certification is in date.

The latest charts and publications used are the most up to date.

The charts used are the largest scale available.

Consult tide atlases and tide tables.

Determine relevant traffic routing schemes.

Consult port guides.

Obtain weather information.

Appraisal

Plot true course on charts.

Consider safe passing distances off land/critical areas. Safe speed.

Alter course points clearly marked.

Methods of position fixing.

Parallel index lines shown.

Contingency plans considered.

Planning

Ship Reporting Systems

KEY POINTS
- ♦ Tend to be of local operation for the safety of navigation.
- ♦ UK ships must comply with IMO adopted reporting systems.

Purpose

- The purpose of ship reporting schemes is to regulate and monitor traffic in areas of particular high density of shipping.

- Ship reporting schemes may also be adopted in areas particularly sensitive to the environment.

- Ship reporting schemes help the safety and efficiency of navigation and contribute to the protection of the environment.

- IMO is responsible for providing the guidelines and criteria for ship reporting schemes. IMO is responsible for approving schemes to be adopted.

- UK ships must comply with mandatory ship reporting schemes adopted anywhere in the world.

- Reports should be made to the shore-based authority when entering a reporting scheme and if required when leaving the scheme.

- Reasons for not reporting e.g. failure of radio communications equipment should be entered in the ships log.

- UK flagged ships are encouraged to comply with Voluntary Reporting Schemes.

- Details of mandatory schemes are found in Admiralty List of Radio Signals and on the relevant Admiralty Chart.

Calais Dover Reporting Scheme (CALDOVREP)

- A mandatory reporting scheme.

- Along with the Traffic Separation Scheme and Channel Navigation Information Service (CNIS) the intention is to assist seafarers in transiting these waters.

- Further information about this scheme can be obtained from the Admiralty List of Radio Signals and the Mariners Routeing Guide.

References:
Safety of Navigation – Regulation 11 (SOLAS V5)
MGN 058 – Ship Reporting Recommendations for the Minches
MGN 128 – Navigation in the Dover Strait
MGN 153 – Compliance with Mandatory Ship reporting Schemes

Ships Routeing

- Established in areas of heavy concentrations of traffic or in environmentally sensitive areas.
- Can be proposed by Contracting Governments for adoption by IMO.
- Schemes may be recommendations for use by ships or they may be mandatory for all or just certain types of vessels.

Considerations

- IMO *Ships Routeing Guide* and The *Annual Summary of Notices to Mariners* list traffic schemes that have been adopted.

- Before using a scheme the Master should take into account the vessels under keel clearance, charted depth and any changes to the seabed that may have occurred since the last survey. The existence of a scheme does not imply that the traffic lane has been adequately surveyed.

- The arrows shown on a chart in a traffic scheme are for guidance only. The vessel does not have to set course by these arrows as long as it is following the general direction of traffic flow.

- In areas where traffic merges vessels should navigate with particular caution. Vessels should at all times have due regard to Rule 10 of the Collision Regulations.

Publications

- IMO *Ships Routeing* details how a routeing scheme is proposed for adoption by IMO and also gives information on those schemes adopted by the organisation.

- Safety of Navigation Regulation 10 Ships *Routeing* gives information on schemes.

- Safety of Navigation Annex V 'Use of IMO Adopted Routeing Schemes'.

- Annual Summary of Notices to Mariners No.17.

Admiralty List of Radio Signals

- Six Volumes - listing worldwide radio information. (See diagram page 16.)

Catalogue of Admiralty Charts and Publications (NP131)

- Details all charts available from the Admiralty and lists all Hydrographic Office publications.

Admiralty Notices to Mariners

- Published weekly by the United Kingdom Hydrographic Office - and contains information required to keep all charts and publications up to date.

Annual Summary of Admiralty Notices to Mariners

- Published at the beginning of each year. Contains all Admiralty Temporary and Preliminary Notices and corrections to Sailing Directions in force on the 1st January. Also contains permanent information on radio messages, navigational warnings distress and rescue at sea and exercise areas.

Cumulative List of Admiralty Notices to Mariners

- Published in January and July. These contain the latest issue date for each chart and any corrections made in the previous two years.

Admiralty Sailing Directions

- Provides essential information for port facilities and coastal navigation. Each book includes the navigation and regulations for the area covered.
- Also includes demographic information on countries and ports: for example - brief history of the country, area and population, language, government, products and trade, currency and public holidays.

Admiralty List of Light and Fog Signals

- Contains details of all lights, light-structures, light-vessel, light-floats, lanbys and light-buoys with lights that elevate greater than 8m. This publication is also available in digital format.

Admiralty Tide Tables

- Published annually in four volumes.

Admiralty List of Radio Signals Contents

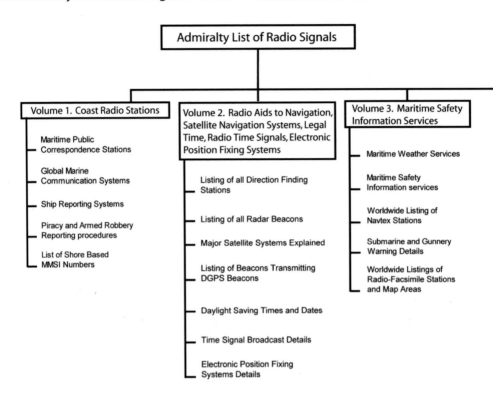

Admiralty List of Radio Signals

Volume 1. Coast Radio Stations
- Maritime Public Correspondence Stations
- Global Marine Communication Systems
- Ship Reporting Systems
- Piracy and Armed Robbery Reporting procedures
- List of Shore Based MMSI Numbers

Volume 2. Radio Aids to Navigation, Satellite Navigation Systems, Legal Time, Radio Time Signals, Electronic Position Fixing Systems
- Listing of all Direction Finding Stations
- Listing of all Radar Beacons
- Major Satellite Systems Explained
- Listing of Beacons Transmitting DGPS Beacons
- Daylight Saving Times and Dates
- Time Signal Broadcast Details
- Electronic Position Fixing Systems Details

Volume 3. Maritime Safety Information Services
- Maritime Weather Services
- Maritime Safety Information services
- Worldwide Listing of Navtex Stations
- Submarine and Gunnery Warning Details
- Worldwide Listings of Radio-Facsimile Stations and Map Areas

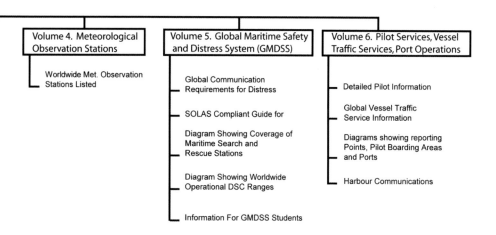

Volume 4. Meteorological Observation Stations
- Worldwide Met. Observation Stations Listed

Volume 5. Global Maritime Safety and Distress System (GMDSS)
- Global Communication Requirements for Distress
- SOLAS Compliant Guide for
- Diagram Showing Coverage of Maritime Search and Rescue Stations
- Diagram Showing Worldwide Operational DSC Ranges
- Information For GMDSS Students

Volume 6. Pilot Services, Vessel Traffic Services, Port Operations
- Detailed Pilot Information
- Global Vessel Traffic Service Information
- Diagrams showing reporting Points, Pilot Boarding Areas and Ports
- Harbour Communications

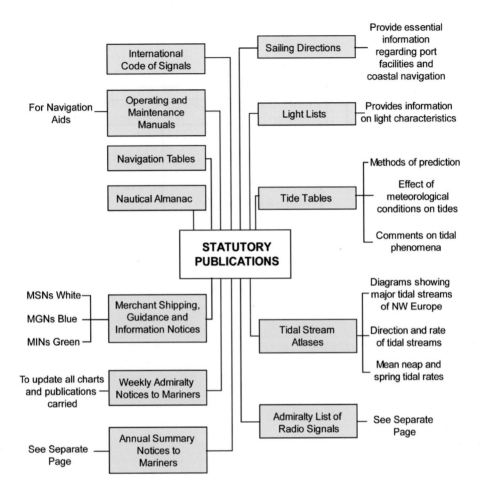

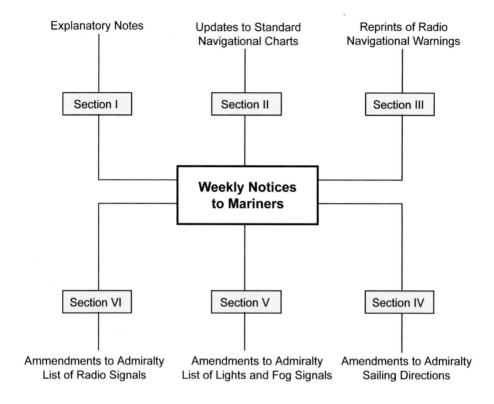

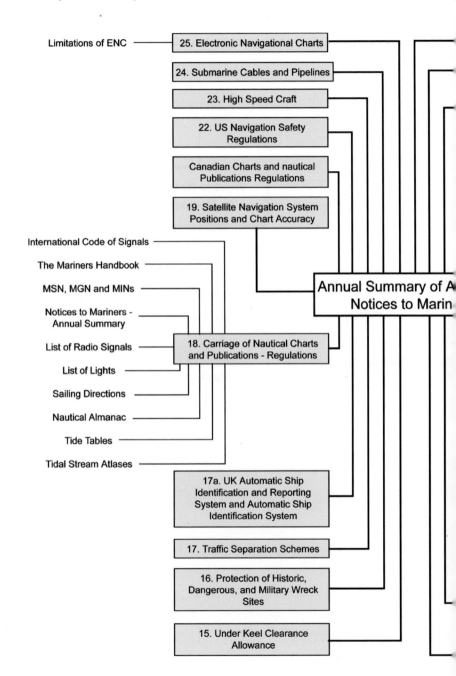

Limitations of ENC ——— 25. Electronic Navigational Charts

24. Submarine Cables and Pipelines

23. High Speed Craft

22. US Navigation Safety Regulations

Canadian Charts and nautical Publications Regulations

19. Satellite Navigation System Positions and Chart Accuracy

International Code of Signals

The Mariners Handbook

MSN, MGN and MINs

Notices to Mariners - Annual Summary

List of Radio Signals

List of Lights

Sailing Directions

Nautical Almanac

Tide Tables

Tidal Stream Atlases

18. Carriage of Nautical Charts and Publications - Regulations

Annual Summary of A Notices to Marin

17a. UK Automatic Ship Identification and Reporting System and Automatic Ship Identification System

17. Traffic Separation Schemes

16. Protection of Historic, Dangerous, and Military Wreck Sites

15. Under Keel Clearance Allowance

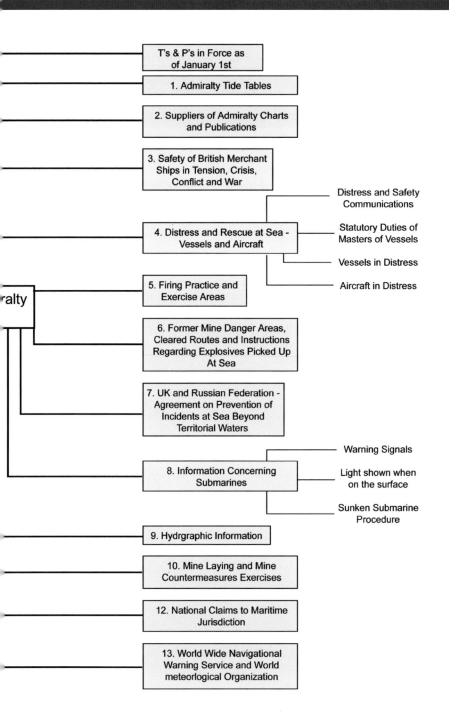

T's & P's in Force as of January 1st

1. Admiralty Tide Tables

2. Suppliers of Admiralty Charts and Publications

3. Safety of British Merchant Ships in Tension, Crisis, Conflict and War

4. Distress and Rescue at Sea - Vessels and Aircraft
- Distress and Safety Communications
- Statutory Duties of Masters of Vessels
- Vessels in Distress
- Aircraft in Distress

5. Firing Practice and Exercise Areas

6. Former Mine Danger Areas, Cleared Routes and Instructions Regarding Explosives Picked Up At Sea

7. UK and Russian Federation - Agreement on Prevention of Incidents at Sea Beyond Territorial Waters

8. Information Concerning Submarines
- Warning Signals
- Light shown when on the surface
- Sunken Submarine Procedure

9. Hydrgraphic Information

10. Mine Laying and Mine Countermeasures Exercises

12. National Claims to Maritime Jurisdiction

13. World Wide Navigational Warning Service and World meteorlogical Organization

ralty

World Wide Navigational Warning Service

KEY POINTS

♦ **Established by International Hydrographic Office (IHO) and International Maritime Organization (IMO).**

♦ **Used to provide the mariner with the latest navigational information.**

♦ **Three types: NAVAREA warnings, Coastal Warnings and Local Warnings.**

NAVAREA Warnings	The world is divided into 16 NAVAREAS. Warnings are issued when there is a need for immediate information regarding new dangers or changes in navigational aids. The Area Co-ordinator will publish the information by the World-wide Navigational Warning Service (WWNWS). Examples include: SAR or anti-pollution; newly discovered wrecks or hazards; positions of mobile drilling rigs.
Coastal Warnings	Information specific to a particular region to assist a navigator in coastal waters up to the harbour entrance. Issued by the National Co-ordinator of the country of origin. Examples include: casualties to major lights; large tows in densely congested waters; cable operations.
Local Warnings	Issued by the port, pilotage or coastguard authorities. The information is specific to local issues.

Reference:
Annual Summary of Admiralty Notices to Mariners
www.iho.org.uk

The Azimuth Mirror

Position Fixing

Take bearings of a terrestrial object - such as a lighthouse - to provide a bearing line for position fixing. Take three bearings of different objects.

Collision Avoidance

Take a bearing of another vessel to determine if there is a risk of a collision. If the bearings are opening, the target is passing astern. If the bearings are closing, the target is passing ahead. Steady bearings = a risk of collision.

Determining the Compass Error

Take a bearing of the sun, a star or planet to determine compass error. Compare the observed bearing of a body with the calculated true bearing to give the compass error.

To Determine the Accuracy of the Azimuth Mirror

For bearings to be accurate, keep the axis of the prism horizontal at all times. The prism is held in place by two small screws: adjust these if the prism loses alignment. To check the accuracy of the mirror, the OOW should observe the same object through the azimuth mirror. Make one observation with the arrow up and one observation with the arrow down. If the bearings are the same no error exists. If there is a difference, an error exists; adjust the prism-holding screws.

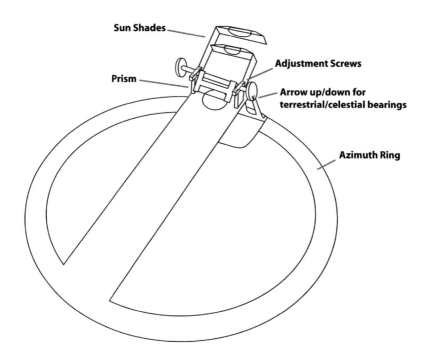

Sun Shades

Prism

Adjustment Screws

Arrow up/down for terrestrial/celestial bearings

Azimuth Ring

Errors of the Sextant

Correctable Errors

Name	Cause	To Correct
Perpendicularity	Index mirror not perpendicular to the plane of the instrument.	Hold the sextant horizontally, arc away from observer's body. Set the index bar half way along the arc. Look into the index mirror so that the 'true' image of the arc and the reflected image can be seen. The 'true' image of the arc and reflected images should be in alignment. If they are not in alignment, there is an error in perpendicularity. To correct, adjust the index mirror screw.
Side Error	Horizon mirror not perpendicular to the plane of the instrument.	Hold the sextant vertically. Observe the altitude of a celestial body. Adjust so that the reflected and direct images of the horizon appear as a continuous line across the horizon glass. Tilt the sextant. If the reflected portion appears above or below the direct part the glass is not perpendicular. Adjust using the two screws behind the horizon glass.
Index Error	Index mirror and horizon mirror not parallel to each other.	Error remaining after perpendicularity and side error corrected for. Set instrument to zero. Look at horizon. Adjust sextant reading so both images of the horizon come into line. The sextant reading when the horizon is in line is the index error. A positive index error should be subtracted and a negative index error should be added.

Non-Correctable Errors

Name	Fault
Prismatic	Two faces of the mirror not parallel to each other.
Worm & Rack	Caused by wear on the gearing rack
Graduation	May be found on the arc, vernier or micrometer scales.
Shade Error	Faces of the shades not parallel to the ground.
Collimation	Axis of telescope not parallel to plane of the sextant.
Centering	Pivot of the index bar is not in the exact centre of the curvature of the arc.

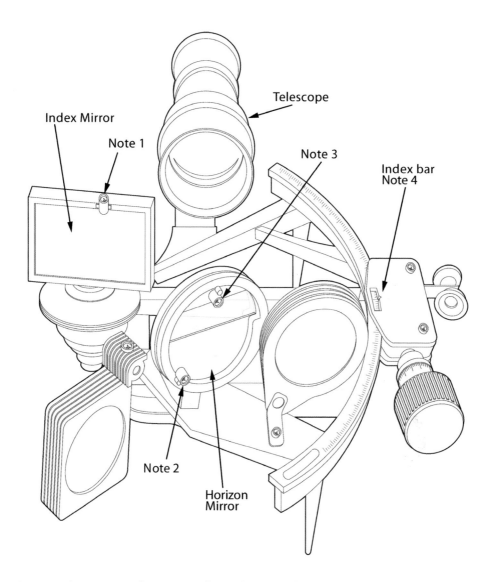

Note 1: Adjustment screw for correction of error of perpendicularity.
Note 2: Adjustment screw for correction of side error.
Note 3: Adjustment screw for side error.
Note 4: Adjustment for index error.

Meterological Instruments

Precision Aneroid Barometer

KEY POINTS

- Check frequently against standing barometers for proper continuous operation.
- Check the PAB every three months as part of planned maintenance routine.
- Apply the correction to reduce the pressure reading to Mean Sea Level (MSL). For this, use reduction tables and allow for the air temperature.
- Barographs should include an efficient built-in damping device. Mount the instrument on shock-absorbing material.

Anemometer

KEY POINTS

- Wind speed: to estimate, use the last ten minutes of observations.
- Site the anemometer as far forward and as high as possible.
- As the anemometer measures the movement of air relative to the ship, use a vector diagram or computer program to find the true wind speed.

Measuring Temperature and Humidity

KEY POINTS

- Keep the wet/dry bulb thermometers in louvered screens, one on each side of the ship. Use the windward one to make the observation.
- Change the muslin and wick fitted to a wet bulb thermometer once a week. More often in stormy weather.
- Place thermometers and hygrometers in a well-ventilated screen with good radiation protection and as far away from any artificial heat as possible.

Reference:
Safety of Navigation Annex 4 – WMO Maritime Services

Shipping Forecast Terminology	
Gale	Winds of at least force 8
Severe Gale	Winds of at least force 9
Storm	Winds of at least force 10
Violent Storm	Winds of at least force 11
Hurricane	Winds of at least force 12
Imminent	Expected within 6 hours of time of issue
Soon	Expected within 6-12 hours of time of issue
Later	Expected more than 12 hours from time of issue
Fog	Visibility less than 1000 metres.
Poor	Visibility between 1000 metres and 2 nautical miles
Moderate	Visibility between 2 and 5 nautical miles
Good	Visibility more than 5 nautical miles
Veering	Wind direction is changing in a clockwise direction
Backing	Wind direction is changing in an anti-clockwise direction

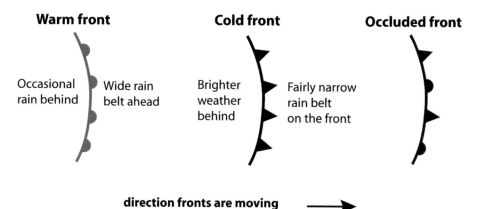

Warm front

Occasional rain behind

Wide rain belt ahead

Cold front

Brighter weather behind

Fairly narrow rain belt on the front

Occluded front

direction fronts are moving ⟶

Warm front	The warm air advancing is replacing the cold air.
Cold front	The cold air advancing replaces the warm air
Occluded front	A result of warm and cold fronts meeting.

Reference:
Mariners Handbook
www.met-office.gov.uk

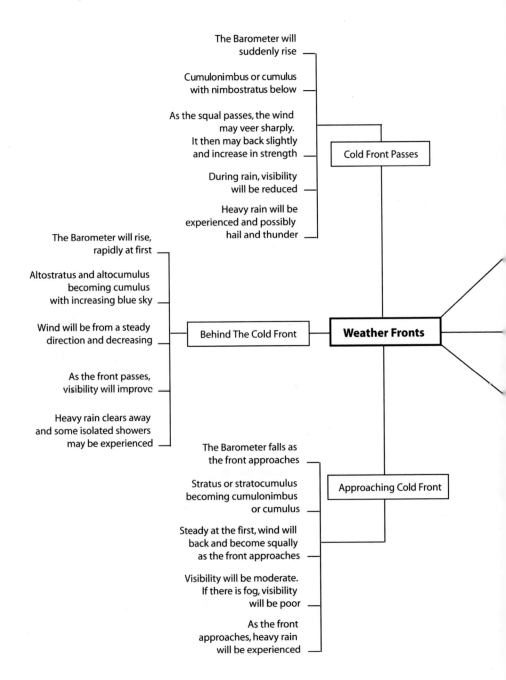

The Barometer will suddenly rise

Cumulonimbus or cumulus with nimbostratus below

As the squal passes, the wind may veer sharply. It then may back slightly and increase in strength

During rain, visibility will be reduced

Heavy rain will be experienced and possibly hail and thunder

Cold Front Passes

The Barometer will rise, rapidly at first

Altostratus and altocumulus becoming cumulus with increasing blue sky

Wind will be from a steady direction and decreasing

As the front passes, visibility will improve

Heavy rain clears away and some isolated showers may be experienced

Behind The Cold Front

Weather Fronts

The Barometer falls as the front approaches

Stratus or stratocumulus becoming cumulonimbus or cumulus

Steady at the first, wind will back and become squally as the front approaches

Visibility will be moderate. If there is fog, visibility will be poor

As the front approaches, heavy rain will be experienced

Approaching Cold Front

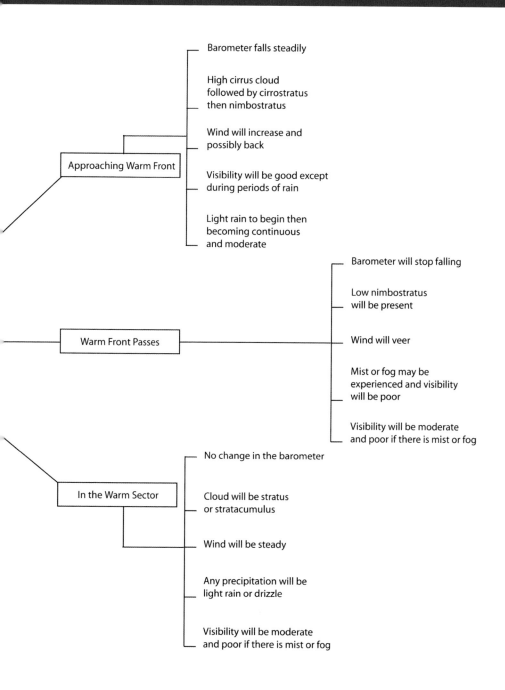

Approaching Warm Front
- Barometer falls steadily
- High cirrus cloud followed by cirrostratus then nimbostratus
- Wind will increase and possibly back
- Visibility will be good except during periods of rain
- Light rain to begin then becoming continuous and moderate

Warm Front Passes
- Barometer will stop falling
- Low nimbostratus will be present
- Wind will veer
- Mist or fog may be experienced and visibility will be poor
- Visibility will be moderate and poor if there is mist or fog

In the Warm Sector
- No change in the barometer
- Cloud will be stratus or stratacumulus
- Wind will be steady
- Any precipitation will be light rain or drizzle
- Visibility will be moderate and poor if there is mist or fog

Establishing the Vessels Location

Wind Observation	Northern Hemisphere	Southern Hemisphere
Veering	Vessel located in dangerous semi-circle.	Vessel located in navigable semi-circle.
If pressure falling: vessel is located in the advance quadrant.		
Backing	Vessel located in navigable semi-circle.	Vessel located in dangerous semi-circle
If pressure falling: vessel is located in the advance quadrant.		
Steady	If pressure is falling, vessel is located in the path of the storm.	

Action by a Vessel in a TRS

Location	Northern Hemisphere	Southern Hemisphere
Dangerous semi-circle	Put the wind on the stbd bow and alter course to starboard as the wind veers.	Put the wind on the port bow and alter course to port as the wind backs.
Navigable semi-circle. In the path of the TRS.	Put the wind on the starboard quarter and alter course to port as the wind backs.	Put the wind on the port quarter and alter course to starboard as the wind veers.

Reference:
Mariners Handbook

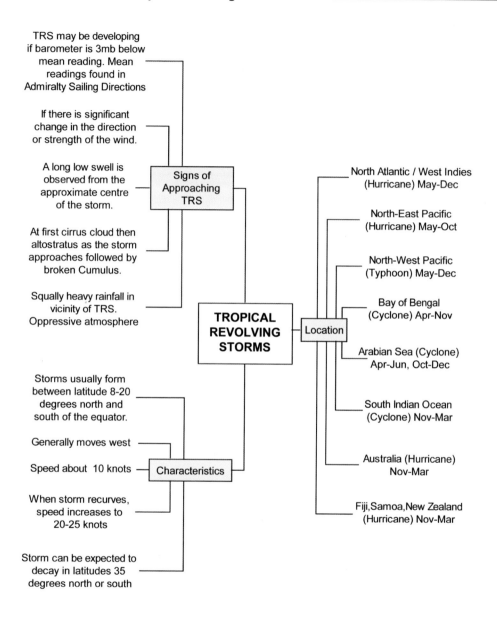

TRS may be developing if barometer is 3mb below mean reading. Mean readings found in Admiralty Sailing Directions

If there is significant change in the direction or strength of the wind.

A long low swell is observed from the approximate centre of the storm.

At first cirrus cloud then altostratus as the storm approaches followed by broken Cumulus.

Squally heavy rainfall in vicinity of TRS. Oppressive atmosphere

Signs of Approaching TRS

Storms usually form between latitude 8-20 degrees north and south of the equator.

Generally moves west

Speed about 10 knots

When storm recurves, speed increases to 20-25 knots

Storm can be expected to decay in latitudes 35 degrees north or south

Characteristics

TROPICAL REVOLVING STORMS

Location

North Atlantic / West Indies (Hurricane) May-Dec

North-East Pacific (Hurricane) May-Oct

North-West Pacific (Typhoon) May-Dec

Bay of Bengal (Cyclone) Apr-Nov

Arabian Sea (Cyclone) Apr-Jun, Oct-Dec

South Indian Ocean (Cyclone) Nov-Mar

Australia (Hurricane) Nov-Mar

Fiji,Samoa,New Zealand (Hurricane) Nov-Mar

Master's Standing Orders

These are written by the master and are specific the particular vessel's characteristics and trade. They clearly indicate the master's requirement for conduct and behaviour among the bridge team. These orders should not conflict with the ship's safety management system.

Before taking over a navigational watch at the commencement of the voyage, the officer should read and sign the standing orders.

	Recording of Navigational Information
Bridge Deck Log Book	• Record position at regular intervals.
	• Record alterations to course and speed.
	• Record weather and sea conditions recorded.
	• Record precautions taken by the vessel in restricted visibility or heavy seas.
	• Record any significant navigational events.
	The Bridge Deck Log Book should be kept onboard the ship or ashore for at least seven years.

Reference:
IMO A.890 (21) 'Principle of Safe Manning'
Safety of Navigation – implementing SOLAS Chapter V Annex 22 –
Recording of Navigational Events.
Bridge Procedures Guide.

Contents of Bridge Procedures Guide

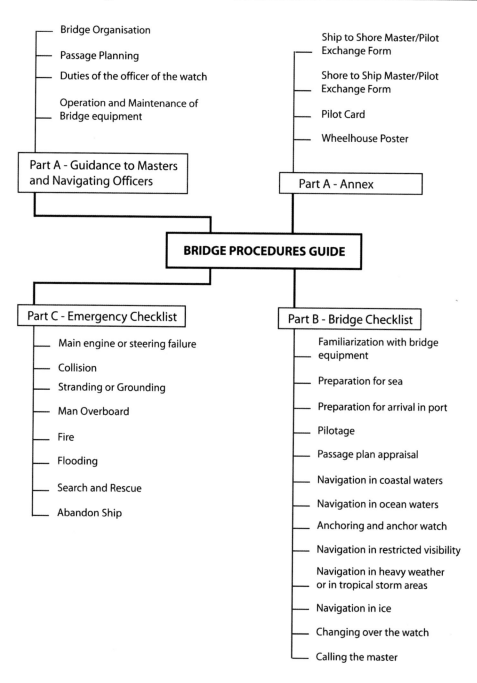

BRIDGE PROCEDURES GUIDE

Part A - Guidance to Masters and Navigating Officers
- Bridge Organisation
- Passage Planning
- Duties of the officer of the watch
- Operation and Maintenance of Bridge equipment

Part A - Annex
- Ship to Shore Master/Pilot Exchange Form
- Shore to Ship Master/Pilot Exchange Form
- Pilot Card
- Wheelhouse Poster

Part C - Emergency Checklist
- Main engine or steering failure
- Collision
- Stranding or Grounding
- Man Overboard
- Fire
- Flooding
- Search and Rescue
- Abandon Ship

Part B - Bridge Checklist
- Familiarization with bridge equipment
- Preparation for sea
- Preparation for arrival in port
- Pilotage
- Passage plan appraisal
- Navigation in coastal waters
- Navigation in ocean waters
- Anchoring and anchor watch
- Navigation in restricted visibility
- Navigation in heavy weather or in tropical storm areas
- Navigation in ice
- Changing over the watch
- Calling the master

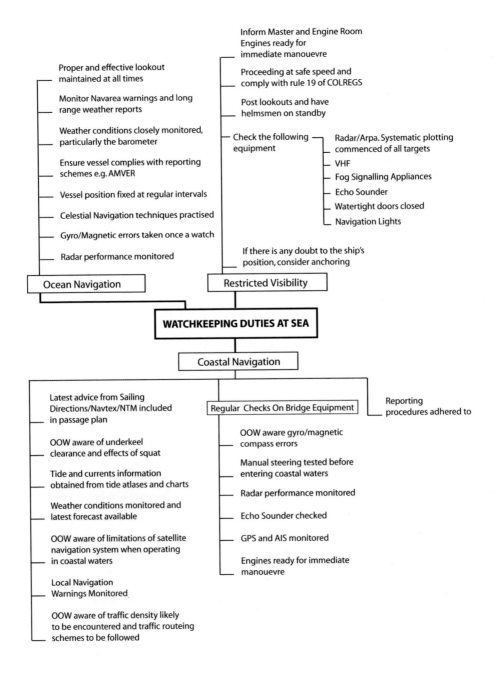

Proper and effective lookout maintained at all times

Monitor Navarea warnings and long range weather reports

Weather conditions closely monitored, particularly the barometer

Ensure vessel complies with reporting schemes e.g. AMVER

Vessel position fixed at regular intervals

Celestial Navigation techniques practised

Gyro/Magnetic errors taken once a watch

Radar performance monitored

Ocean Navigation

Inform Master and Engine Room Engines ready for immediate manouevre

Proceeding at safe speed and comply with rule 19 of COLREGS

Post lookouts and have helmsmen on standby

Check the following equipment
— Radar/Arpa. Systematic plotting commenced of all targets
— VHF
— Fog Signalling Appliances
— Echo Sounder
— Watertight doors closed
— Navigation Lights

If there is any doubt to the ship's position, consider anchoring

Restricted Visibility

WATCHKEEPING DUTIES AT SEA

Coastal Navigation

Latest advice from Sailing Directions/Navtex/NTM included in passage plan

OOW aware of underkeel clearance and effects of squat

Tide and currents information obtained from tide atlases and charts

Weather conditions monitored and latest forecast available

OOW aware of limitations of satellite navigation system when operating in coastal waters

Local Navigation Warnings Monitored

OOW aware of traffic density likely to be encountered and traffic routeing schemes to be followed

Regular Checks On Bridge Equipment

OOW aware gyro/magnetic compass errors

Manual steering tested before entering coastal waters

Radar performance monitored

Echo Sounder checked

GPS and AIS monitored

Engines ready for immediate manouevre

Reporting procedures adhered to

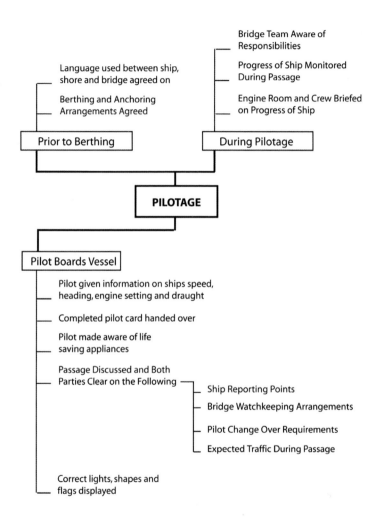

Bridge Team Aware of
Responsibilities

Progress of Ship Monitored
During Passage

Engine Room and Crew Briefed
on Progress of Ship

Language used between ship,
shore and bridge agreed on

Berthing and Anchoring
Arrangements Agreed

Prior to Berthing

During Pilotage

PILOTAGE

Pilot Boards Vessel

Pilot given information on ships speed,
heading, engine setting and draught

Completed pilot card handed over

Pilot made aware of life
saving appliances

Passage Discussed and Both
Parties Clear on the Following

Ship Reporting Points

Bridge Watchkeeping Arrangements

Pilot Change Over Requirements

Expected Traffic During Passage

Correct lights, shapes and
flags displayed

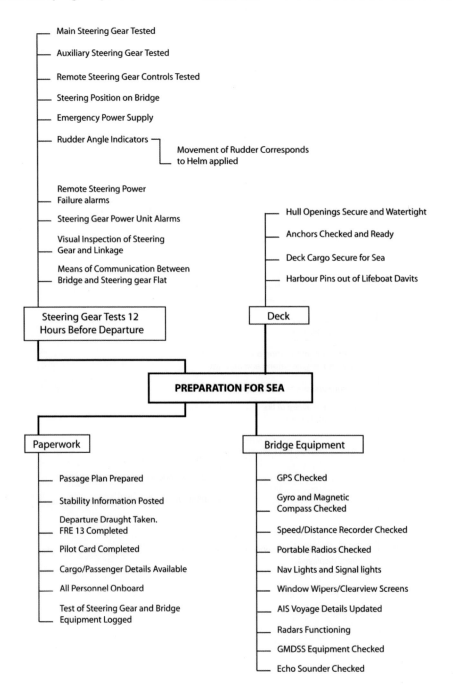

Main Steering Gear Tested

Auxiliary Steering Gear Tested

Remote Steering Gear Controls Tested

Steering Position on Bridge

Emergency Power Supply

Rudder Angle Indicators — Movement of Rudder Corresponds to Helm applied

Remote Steering Power Failure alarms

Steering Gear Power Unit Alarms

Visual Inspection of Steering Gear and Linkage

Means of Communication Between Bridge and Steering gear Flat

Steering Gear Tests 12 Hours Before Departure

Hull Openings Secure and Watertight

Anchors Checked and Ready

Deck Cargo Secure for Sea

Harbour Pins out of Lifeboat Davits

Deck

PREPARATION FOR SEA

Paperwork

Passage Plan Prepared

Stability Information Posted

Departure Draught Taken. FRE 13 Completed

Pilot Card Completed

Cargo/Passenger Details Available

All Personnel Onboard

Test of Steering Gear and Bridge Equipment Logged

Bridge Equipment

GPS Checked

Gyro and Magnetic Compass Checked

Speed/Distance Recorder Checked

Portable Radios Checked

Nav Lights and Signal lights

Window Wipers/Clearview Screens

AIS Voyage Details Updated

Radars Functioning

GMDSS Equipment Checked

Echo Sounder Checked

Watchkeeping in Port and at Anchor

Taking Over a Watch in Port

Ensure you are satisfied with the following:

Depth of the water at the berth, vessel draught

Mooring arrangements

State of engine readiness in an emergency

All work to be performed on the vessel both cargo and maintenance. Permits to work in force

Number of crew members required to be onboard

State of fire fighting appliances

Any special port regulations

Masters standing orders

Watchkeeping in Port

Make frequent rounds of the vessel

Check the gangway and ensure it is secure and provides a safe access

Check the moorings. Be aware of tidal conditions throughout the watch

Be aware of the vessel draught and planned cargo/ballasting activities throughout the watch

Awareness of the latest weather forecasts and expected sea state

Ensure vessel complies with fire and safety regulations

Know where contractors/ship staff are working on the vessel. Particularly work being carried out in enclosed spaces

Ensure no work is being carried out without a valid permit to work

Take every precaution to prevent pollution of the enviroment by the ship

Update information in the fire wallet with crew manifest and stability as required

In an emergency, raise the alarm, call the master and instigate measures to prevent damage to the ship, people onboard and cargo

Ensure nothing is obstructing the propellers when they are about to be turned

Prior to departure obtain draught for FRE13 form

Make a log of all important events

At Anchor

Plot the vessel's position on the largest scale chart available

Frequently check the vessel's position using visual bearings, ranges or transits

Ensure proper lookout is maintained at all times

Ensure engines are available as specified by the master in case vessel starts to drag anchor

Ensure ship is exhibiting necessary lights and shapes and sounding appropriate signal as required

Frequent security rounds made of the vessel

Observe meteorological and tidal conditions

Notify the master and take necessary action if vessel starts to drag anchor

Notify master if visibility deteriorates

Ensure ship is taking all measures to protect the enviroment from pollution from the vessel

Reference:
STCW 95 Chapter 8

Definitions

Heading Control System – a vessels autopilot. Track Control System – the vessel is kept on a pre-determined track and uses an input from a satellite navigation system.

Operation

Casualties have occurred through over reliance of the autopilot. Consider these points:

- Keep an effective lookout at all times.
- The OOW should be familiar with the change-over procedure.
- Label all operating functions clearly.
- Only use a heading control system or track control system in areas of high traffic density, restricted visibility or navigation critical areas when the change-over to manual can be completed within 30 seconds. Post clear change-over instructions next to the console. In such areas, the OOW should use both steering gear power units.

- The OOW should be aware of the use of parameters such as, rudder; counter rudder and weather to ensure the vessel maintains an optimum heading performance.

Testing

- Test manual steering at sea at least once a day and before entering restricted waters.
- Test steering gear at least twelve hours before departure. If vessel is on regular short voyages, this may be done once a week.
- Log all steering gear tests, checks and emergency steering drills in the Official Logbook (if carried). This should be available for inspection.
- Perform an emergency steering gear drill every three months. Enter details in the log. (Emergency steering gear drill within 24 hours of entry to the USA).

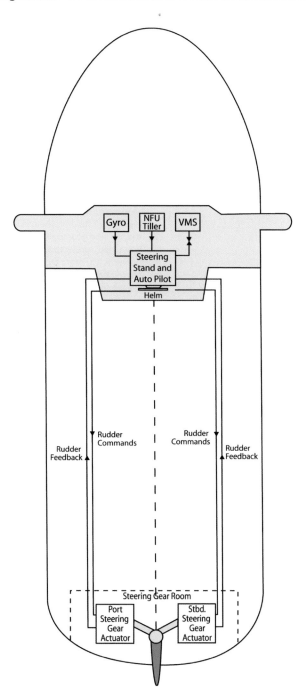

Steering Modes

Autopilot

Rudder command signals to steer the ship are produced by an electronic device. The navigator will set the required course into the autopilot. The autopilot then compares the 'set course' with information received from the gyrocompass. If there is a difference, a rudder command signal causes the rudder to move and bring the ship back on course.

An autopilot has controls to counteract the effects of:

1. Yaw
2. Trim
3. Draft
4. Weather

Autopilot Features

Rudder Limit

- Sets a limit on the rudder angle applied by automatic control.

Rudder

- Controls the number of degrees the rudder will move to correct every degree of heading error. For example: with the control set to 3, the rudder will move 3° for every 1° of heading error.

Counter Rudder

- Determines the amount of opposite helm to be applied. Control is adjusted to suit prevailing conditions.

Weather

- Control to counteract the effect of weather and sea conditions. This control imposes a time-delay on the rudder command signal so that the ship will recover naturally when under the influence of repetitive yaw. The overall effect is to increase the amplitude of yaw that can be tolerated before the steering gear is enabled.

Manual Steering – Follow-Up Mode

The rudder is normally at the amidships position. If the wheel is moved to port or starboard, rudder voltage is produced. This voltage starts the steering gear and moves the rudder. If the wheel is put to 25° to port, the rudder voltage will move the steering gear to this angle. Once 25° to port is reached, an electrical signal from the rudder prevents any more movement. If the wheel is now moved back to amidships, the rudder will 'follow' the wheel.

Manual Steering – Non-Follow-Up Mode

Non-Follow-Up is operated by a control lever that is separate from the ship's wheel. To set the rudder angle to 25° to port, move the lever to 25° to port. The rudder then moves to port. The control lever returns to amidships - but the rudder stays at 25° port. To return the rudder to amidships, use the lever to apply opposite helm.

Emergency Steering

Every vessel shall have a means of steering independent from the main steering. The vessel should have communications from the bridge to the steering flat to allow the order and response of helm orders.

Automated Identification System

KEY POINTS

♦ To help identify vessels. To assist in target tracking. To automatically exchange mandatory ship-reporting information. Improve the quality of information available to the OOW to enable more effective decision-making.

♦ AIS continuously transmits the ship's own data to other vessels and VTS stations. It also continuously receives data from other vessels and VTS stations and, when linked to radar or ECDIS, can display this data.

♦ All ships over 300 gt engaged in International voyages to have AIS fitted.

♦ AIS should be in operation at all times - except where there is a need for navigational information to be protected under international agreements, rules or standards.

♦ AIS may be switched off if the Master believes it would compromise the security of his ship. If this occurs within a mandatory reporting system, the Master should report this action and the reason to the competent authority. If AIS is switched off, note it in the log and add the reason. Restore the AIS as soon as it is safe to do so.

Information Transmitted

Static Data	Dynamic Data	Voyage Data
MMSI Number	Ships position and accuracy of fix indication	Ships draught
Call sign and name	Position time stamp in UTC	Hazardous cargo (Type)
IMO number	Course over ground	Destination and ETA
Length and Beam	Speed over ground	Route Plan (waypoints)
Type of ship	Heading	
Location of position fixing antenna	Navigational Status	
	Rate of Turn	

Checks

- Once a month, check ship's static information is correct and up to date. Data changed on Master's authority.

- Check dynamic information: position accuracy of GPS, speed-over-ground and sensor information.

- To check this information, contact other vessels or shore stations.

Limitations

- Note that other ships, leisure craft, warships and coastal stations, VTS centres may not be fitted with AIS.

- Although the ship may be within a reporting system, it may be out of VHF range. Typical VHF range 20-30 miles

- Information in the mandatory report may be more than the information given out by the AIS

- Ships fitted with AIS may have it switched off by professional judgement of master.

- AIS may not be a complete picture of the situation around the ship.

- Identification of a target by AIS does not overcome problems associated in using VHF to discuss action to avoid collision.

- AIS uses a Global Navigation Satellite System to derive positions. This may not coincide with the radar target.

- Faulty input to the AIS may lead to incorrect information being displayed on other vessels.

- Correct identification of other vessels does not eliminate the dangers of using the VHF for collision avoidance. (MGN 167 – Dangers in the use of VHF in collision avoidance.)

Reference:
Safety of Navigation implementing SOLAS Chapter 5 – Annex 17
MGN 277 (M+F) Operational Guidance for Automatic Identification Systems (AIS) on Board Ship.

ECDIS	
Raster Navigational Chart (RNC)	**Electronic Navigational Chart (RNC)**
A digital scan of a paper chart	Compiled from a database of information this presents the OOW with a seamless vector chart.
Displayed on an electronic chart display. With GPS input the vessels position can be shown.	
	Information is built up in layers and the OOW can decide not to view certain features in order to keep the view clear and simple.
Alarms are not automatically triggered An alarm will only sound if the user has previously highlighted a danger at the voyage plan stage and inputted the information into the electronic display.	
	Alarms will automatically trigger in response to information inputted regarding the vessel draught and required underkeel clearance or proximity to hazards.
Be aware that the chart datum may differ between RNCs which could result in discrepancies in the vessels position.	Provides an indication as to the quality of data in use.
Features cannot be removed for simplicity as in ENC charts.	Can provide the OOW with additional Info e.g. light characteristics, tidal information.
RNC charts offer limited ability to scan ahead.	All ENC charts are referred to the WGS84 spheriod and therefore compatible with GPS.
As an RNC chart is a scanned image of a paper chart it should be viewed at the same scale as the paper chart. There is no advantage in excessive zooming.	
	The vessel must carry out a risk assessment to determine how many paper charts have to be carried onboard if this system is in use.
The satellite position received may be more accurate than the chart data.	
Vessel must carry appropriate folio of back up charts.	

- ECDIS is an Electronic Chart Display Information System.
- ECDIS can operate either ENC charts or with RNC charts.
- When ECDIS is using RNC charts it is operating in Raster Chart Display System mode (RCDS).

Reference:
Safety of Navigation Annex 14 – Electronic Charts
MGN 194 (M+F) Electronic Charts

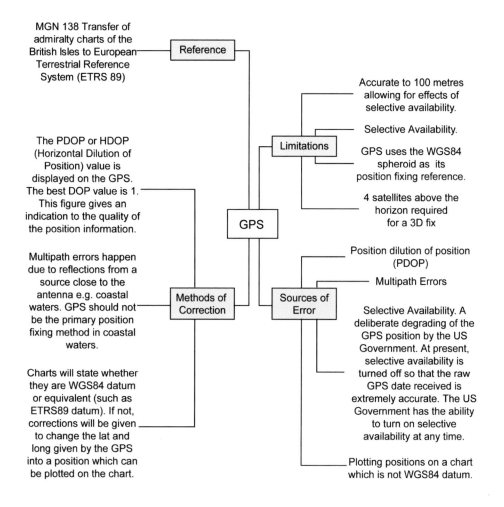

MGN 138 Transfer of admiralty charts of the British Isles to European Terrestrial Reference System (ETRS 89)

Reference

The PDOP or HDOP (Horizontal Dilution of Position) value is displayed on the GPS. The best DOP value is 1. This figure gives an indication to the quality of the position information.

Multipath errors happen due to reflections from a source close to the antenna e.g. coastal waters. GPS should not be the primary position fixing method in coastal waters.

Charts will state whether they are WGS84 datum or equivalent (such as ETRS89 datum). If not, corrections will be given to change the lat and long given by the GPS into a position which can be plotted on the chart.

Methods of Correction

GPS

Limitations

Accurate to 100 metres allowing for effects of selective availability.

Selective Availability.

GPS uses the WGS84 spheroid as its position fixing reference.

4 satellites above the horizon required for a 3D fix

Sources of Error

Position dilution of position (PDOP)

Multipath Errors

Selective Availability. A deliberate degrading of the GPS position by the US Government. At present, selective availability is turned off so that the raw GPS date received is extremely accurate. The US Government has the ability to turn on selective availability at any time.

Plotting positions on a chart which is not WGS84 datum.

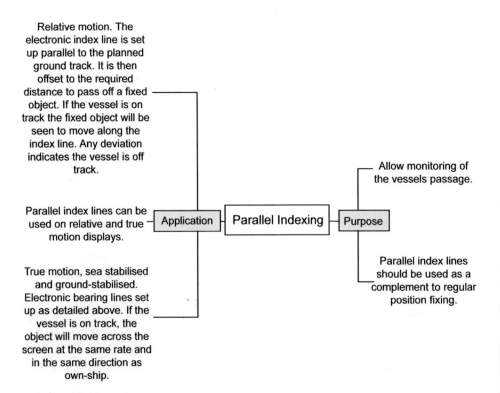

Relative motion. The electronic index line is set up parallel to the planned ground track. It is then offset to the required distance to pass off a fixed object. If the vessel is on track the fixed object will be seen to move along the index line. Any deviation indicates the vessel is off track.

Parallel index lines can be used on relative and true motion displays.

True motion, sea stabilised and ground-stabilised. Electronic bearing lines set up as detailed above. If the vessel is on track, the object will move across the screen at the same rate and in the same direction as own-ship.

Application — Parallel Indexing — Purpose

Allow monitoring of the vessels passage.

Parallel index lines should be used as a complement to regular position fixing.

| **RADAR** |

| **3cm, X-Band, 9 GHZ** | **10cm, S-Band, 3 GHZ** |

In fair weather a target will show up better on a 9 Ghz radar

Can detect a Search and Rescue Transponder (SART) at range approx. 8 miles.

Better at detecting targets in rain

Radar horizon greater than 9 Ghz radar. Better for long range detection of targets

Sea clutter response better than 9 Ghz. Therefore targets are less likely to be hidden.

Checks

Check the radar's performance monitor at every 4 hours.

- When using the radar for position fixing, positively identify all objects used for ranges/ bearings. Ranges are more accurate than bearings. Do not rely on a single range and bearing for position.

- Check the gyro error and check that the heading marker is aligned with the compass heading of the ship.

- Check the accuracy of the variable range marker, bearing cursor and fixed range rings.

- Be aware of blind and shadow sectors. These should be printed on a diagram and located close to the radar.

- When radar is used for collision avoidance, the speed input should be from a water-stabilised source, such as the log. The speed given by GPS is ground-stabilised.

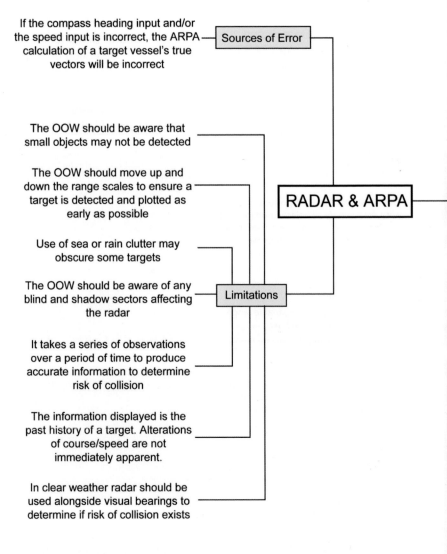

If the compass heading input and/or the speed input is incorrect, the ARPA calculation of a target vessel's true vectors will be incorrect

Sources of Error

The OOW should be aware that small objects may not be detected

The OOW should move up and down the range scales to ensure a target is detected and plotted as early as possible

Use of sea or rain clutter may obscure some targets

The OOW should be aware of any blind and shadow sectors affecting the radar

It takes a series of observations over a period of time to produce accurate information to determine risk of collision

The information displayed is the past history of a target. Alterations of course/speed are not immediately apparent.

In clear weather radar should be used alongside visual bearings to determine if risk of collision exists

Limitations

RADAR & ARPA

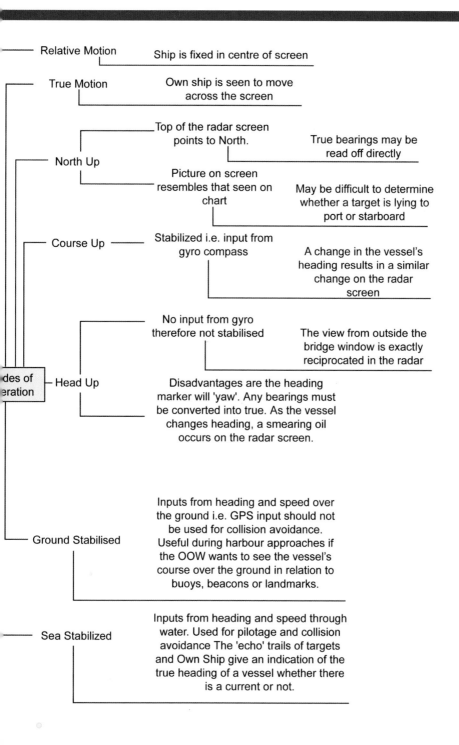

Relative Motion — Ship is fixed in centre of screen

True Motion — Own ship is seen to move across the screen

North Up
- Top of the radar screen points to North. — True bearings may be read off directly
- Picture on screen resembles that seen on chart — May be difficult to determine whether a target is lying to port or starboard

Course Up — Stabilized i.e. input from gyro compass — A change in the vessel's heading results in a similar change on the radar screen

Head Up
- No input from gyro therefore not stabilised — The view from outside the bridge window is exactly reciprocated in the radar
- Disadvantages are the heading marker will 'yaw'. Any bearings must be converted into true. As the vessel changes heading, a smearing oil occurs on the radar screen.

Modes of operation

Ground Stabilised — Inputs from heading and speed over the ground i.e. GPS input should not be used for collision avoidance. Useful during harbour approaches if the OOW wants to see the vessel's course over the ground in relation to buoys, beacons or landmarks.

Sea Stabilized — Inputs from heading and speed through water. Used for pilotage and collision avoidance The 'echo' trails of targets and Own Ship give an indication of the true heading of a vessel whether there is a current or not.

Purpose

Used to provide a recording of key operational events throughout a 12 hour period. Events recorded include: radar, voice, DGPS, engine orders and weather information. In the event of an incident involving the ship, these recordings may be used to analyse events.

The information is recorded in a protective capsule. In the event of a casualty, this may be recovered. The protective capsule records information continuously and will always have 12 hours information stored.

Annual Test

- To ensure data is recorded and being replayed reliably.

- Inspect onboard equipment. Check that batteries, enclosures and location aids are in good condition.

- Record the completed results the planned maintenance log.

- Download a 12-hour period of the ship when the majority of sensors were exercised and send it to the manufacturer for analysis. This analysis will confirm the accuracy, duration and recoverability of the recorded data. If the results are satisfactory, a certificate will be issued and held onboard.

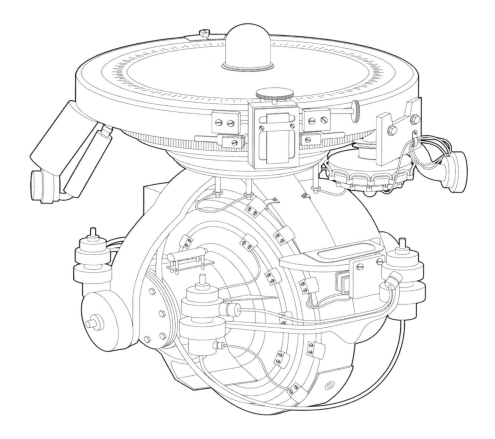

Checks to be Made

- The datum line at the base of the repeaters is aligned with the fore and aft axis of the vessel. Perform any realignment before the ship sails.

- All repeaters should be within 0.5° of the gyrocompass.

- Take a compass error and record it in the compass error book at least once a watch.

- When the vessel is on passage, correct the gyro for latitude and speed error.

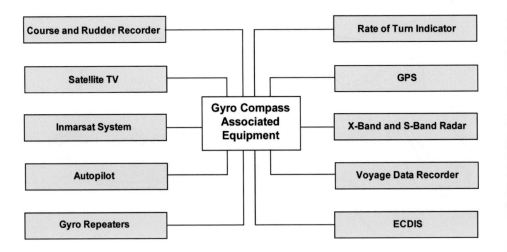

Compass Adjustment

- Adjust the magnetic compass when it is first installed.
- If the compass becomes unreliable, re-adjust it.
- Any structural repairs or alterations to the ship may affect the vessel's permanent and induced magnetism. Adjust the compass on completion of the repairs or alterations.
- If any electrical or magnetic equipment has been fitted near to the compass, adjust the compass.
- If more than two years have passed since the last compass adjustment took place (and a record of compass deviations has not been maintained) adjust the compass.

Performance Checks

The performance of the magnetic compass should be checked:

- After the vessel has carried a cargo with magnetic properties.
- If any electromagnetic lifting appliances have been used to load or discharge the vessel.
- If the ship has been involved in a collision or incident, which may cause major structural damage.
- If the vessel has been laid up for a period of time.

Operational Checks

- Check the gimbal is moving freely.
- Check the compass card is clear and sharp. Card should float freely and rotate without any friction.
- Check the liquid is free of bubbles and clear. No liquid leaks around seals or filler plugs.

Monitoring Performance

- Record compass deviations in the 'Compass Deviation Book.'
- Take a compass error after every large alteration of course.
- Record a compass error at least once a watch.
- The purpose of taking a compass error is to identify any excessive deviations, which may indicate the need for repair.

Compass Adjustment

- Only adjusted by a compass adjuster holding a *Certificate of Competency as Compass Adjuster.*
- If a certified adjuster is unavailable, the compass may be adjusted by a person holding a *certificate of Competency (Deck Officer) Class 1.*

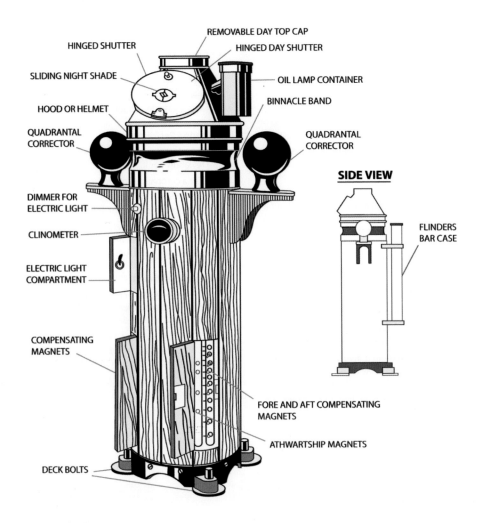

REMOVABLE DAY TOP CAP

HINGED SHUTTER

HINGED DAY SHUTTER

SLIDING NIGHT SHADE

OIL LAMP CONTAINER

HOOD OR HELMET

BINNACLE BAND

QUADRANTAL CORRECTOR

QUADRANTAL CORRECTOR

DIMMER FOR ELECTRIC LIGHT

CLINOMETER

ELECTRIC LIGHT COMPARTMENT

COMPENSATING MAGNETS

FORE AND AFT COMPENSATING MAGNETS

ATHWARTSHIP MAGNETS

DECK BOLTS

SIDE VIEW

FLINDERS BAR CASE

Correcting the Compass

1. Flinders bar. Vertical soft iron corrector. A soft iron vertical bar correcting for vertical soft iron abaft of the compass. Most common vertical soft iron on the ship is the funnel.

2. Spheres. Quadrantal Soft Iron Correctors. The flinders bar produces a small quantity of fore and aft, horizontal and vertical effect on the compass. The soft iron spheres correct for these errors.

3. Heeling error. Compensated by permanent magnets set vertically in a bucket beneath the compass.

4. Horizontal magnets. Permanent fore and aft corrector magnets. Permanent athwartships corrector magnets.

Prior to Anchoring

1. Perform risk assessment. Consult chart of preferred holding ground for mud or clay. Determine prevailing weather conditions.

2. Mark proposed anchoring position on the chart. Slow down positions. Be aware of the contingency plan.

3. For the length of cable required, determine the 'scope'. As a general guide, multiply the square root of the depth of water in metres x 2. The result = the number of shackles to use.

4. Brief bridge team, anchor party and engine room on duties.

Approaching Anchorage

1. Monitor the charted track. Use parallel indexing and transit bearings if practical.

2. Monitor traffic conditions.

3. Observe other vessels at anchor to determine wind, current direction.

4. Approach with wind approximately a point on the bow, if there is no wind stem the current.

5. Check communications with all parties.

Letting go the Anchor

1. Reduce speed at points indicated on the chart. To take way off and induce astern movement give a kick astern at the 'let go' position. When wash of the vessel going astern is level with the bridge wing inform the focsle to 'let go' anchor.

2. Stop the engines. Vessel will move astern as the cable is laid out in a line. When anchor touches the seabed take cross bearings and note position. Anchor facility in GPS may be used as a cross check. Raise anchor ball.

3. Once the required amount of shackles paid out the brake is applied to the windlass and the vessel is brought up.

Definitions

Short stay – the anchor cable is almost vertical.
Long stay – the anchor cable is almost horizontal.
Brought up – when the anchor is holding and the cable has a good catenary.

Effect of Wind and Current

When a vessel is in a wind, consider these factors: displacement of the vessel, whether it is laden or in ballast. Also consider the type of vessel and how much windage area she has.

When a vessel is stopped, she will lie beam-on to the wind.

Current

The current affects all ships equally, regardless of the specific characteristics of a vessel.

When a vessel is berthed or at anchor, the ship's position can be affected by a current flowing round the rudder.

When berthing, a vessel should try to stem the current and take advantage of the braking effect.

Direction of Wind	Effect on Vessel
Ahead	Vessel easily steered. Easily stopped.
On the bow	Constant weather helm required. Vessel will have tendency to 'crab' due to the leeway experienced.
On the beam	Maximum leeway experienced.
On the quarter	Vessel will try to cross the wind. Constant lee helm required to prevent the bow turning towards the wind direction.
Astern	Easy to steer. Difficult to stop vessel.

Bank Effect

- Occurs when a vessel is navigating close to a gently shelving bank.
- Forces caused by the flow of water between the vessel and the bank may push the bow away and draw the stern towards the bank.
- A large positive pressure area at the bow that forces it away from the bank may cause this effect.
- Bank effect is also caused by fast flowing water at the stern creating a suction effect that draws the stern in towards the bank.
- Bank effect may occur in a river or when the vessel is near a shoal area.

Bow Cushion Effect

- If the river is steep sided, the effect of the pressure build-up at the bow is known as 'Bow Cushion.'
- This effect can assist the vessel when approaching a bend in a river or canal. Balance the effect of the bow being pushed away by applying helm towards the bank.
- Approaching a bank on the starboard side of the vessel, a right hand screw propeller would increase the effect of bow cushion.

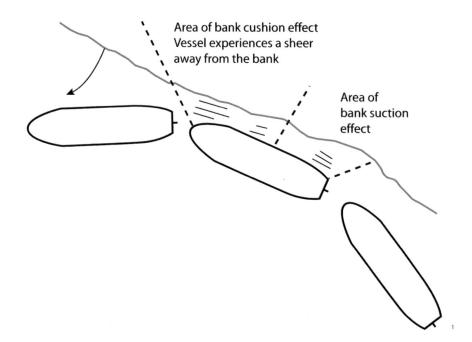

Area of bank cushion effect
Vessel experiences a sheer away from the bank

Area of bank suction effect

¹ *Reproduced from Seamanship Techniques, David House ref fig. 9.47*

Standing Moor

KEY POINTS
- **Stem the tide.**
- **Let go leeward anchor first.**

1. Amend the passage plan to identify the depth of water and holding ground.
2. As the leeward anchor is 'let go', give the vessel a kick astern. As the vessel moves astern, twice as much cable as required is paid out.
3. Vessel stops. Bow is canted away from the leeward anchor. 'Let go' windward anchor.
4. When vessel heaves on leeward anchor, use engines in bursts to move ahead. The windward anchor is paid out.
5. Pay out on the windward anchor and heave on the leeward anchor until the vessel is brought up between the two.

1 Stem the tide, let go lee anchor

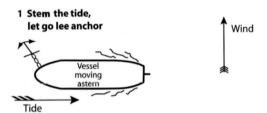

Wind

Vessel moving astern

Tide

2 Pay out on cable, let go second anchor

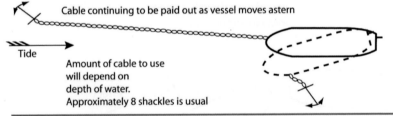

Cable continuing to be paid out as vessel moves astern

Tide

Amount of cable to use will depend on depth of water. Approximately 8 shackles is usual

3 Pay out second anchor cable heave in on first cable

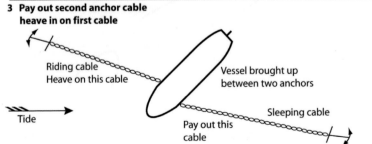

Riding cable
Heave on this cable

Vessel brought up between two anchors

Tide

Pay out this cable

Sleeping cable

2

---

² *Reproduced from Seamanship Techniques, David House ref fig. 9.40*

1. Amend the passage plan to identify the depth of water and holding ground.

2. Vessel speed = 4-5 knots. At point identified on chart, 'let go' windward anchor. Vessel will be blown away from anchor cable

3. As the vessel moves ahead, pay out twice the amount of cable required to hold the vessel. If the vessel determines four shackles of cable is required, pay out eight shackles as you move ahead.

4. Vessel stops and moves astern. 'Let go' leeside anchor. As vessel moves astern, pay out on leeside anchor and pick up on windward anchor.

5. Vessel is brought up between the two anchors.

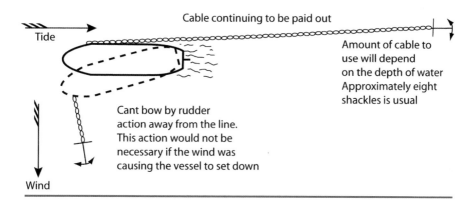

Tide

Cable continuing to be paid out

Amount of cable to use will depend on the depth of water Approximately eight shackles is usual

Cant bow by rudder action away from the line. This action would not be necessary if the wind was causing the vessel to set down

Wind

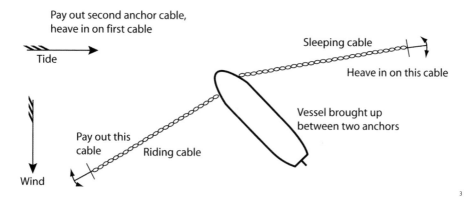

Pay out second anchor cable, heave in on first cable

Tide

Sleeping cable

Heave in on this cable

Vessel brought up between two anchors

Pay out this cable

Riding cable

Wind

3

³ Reproduced from *Seamanship Techniques, David House ref fig. 9.40*

Berthing Port Side to No Wind No Tide

1. Approach at angle of 25° - 30°. Dead slow ahead.

2. One vessel length from berth. Stop engines. Set rudder to starboard. Reverse propulsion.

3. When vessel stops in water, effects of the transverse thrust will bring vessel parallel to quay

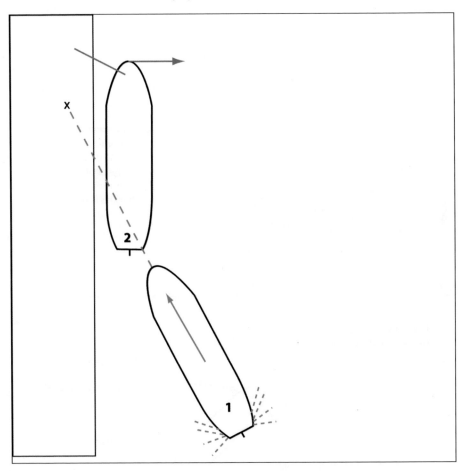

Starboard Side To No Wind No Tide

1. Approach at a shallow angle about 10°. Dead slow ahead.

2. One vessel length from berth, give a kick ahead and set the rudder to port. Reverse propulsion and take off the way.

3. Transverse thrust acts against vessel. Kick ahead induces swing to port before vessel is stopped parallel to berth.

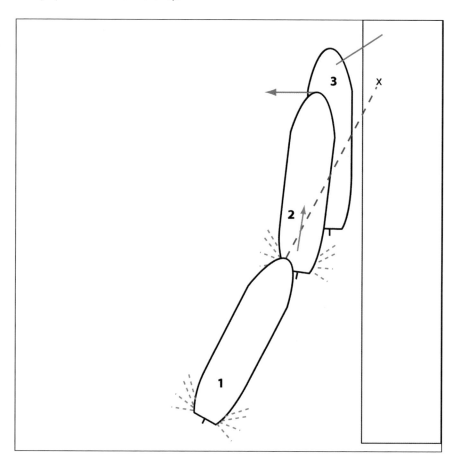

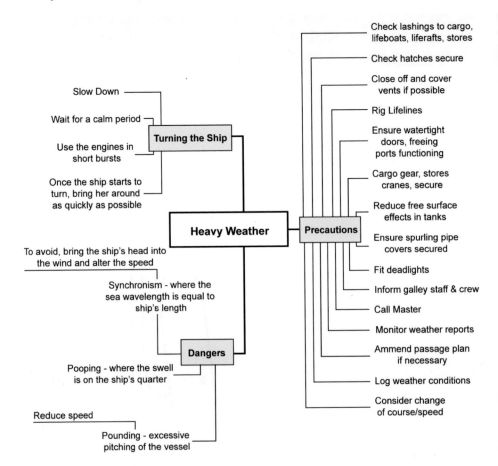

Slow Down

Wait for a calm period

Use the engines in short bursts

Once the ship starts to turn, bring her around as quickly as possible

Turning the Ship

To avoid, bring the ship's head into the wind and alter the speed

Synchronism - where the sea wavelength is equal to ship's length

Heavy Weather

Precautions

Dangers

Pooping - where the swell is on the ship's quarter

Reduce speed

Pounding - excessive pitching of the vessel

Check lashings to cargo, lifeboats, liferafts, stores

Check hatches secure

Close off and cover vents if possible

Rig Lifelines

Ensure watertight doors, freeing ports functioning

Cargo gear, stores cranes, secure

Reduce free surface effects in tanks

Ensure spurling pipe covers secured

Fit deadlights

Inform galley staff & crew

Call Master

Monitor weather reports

Ammend passage plan if necessary

Log weather conditions

Consider change of course/speed

Vessels Approaching Head On

1. The positive pressure at the bow of each vessel causes the bows to be repelled.

2. When abeam, the low pressure areas along the side of each vessel creates a suction effect - and if the vessels are passing too close, a collision can occur.

3. When the bow of each vessel is at the stern of the other, the vessels will sheer towards each other and the positive pressure at the bow will cause the sterns pushed away.

4. As the vessels move clear of each other, the low pressure areas along the sides of each vessel will draw their sterns together and help each vessel to regain its original track.

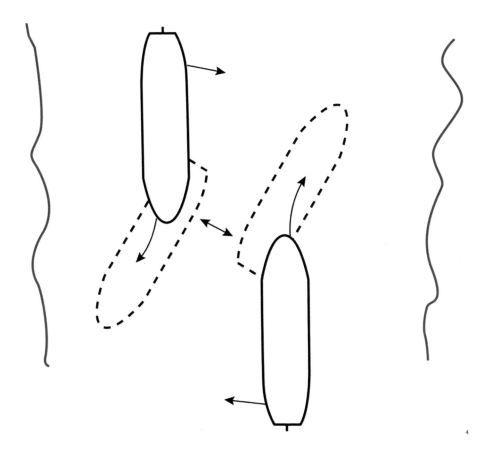

⁴ Reproduced from *Seamanship Techniques, David House ref fig. 9.46*

Vessels Overtaking

1. Due to the positive pressure at the bow of the overtaking vessel the vessel being overtaken may take a sheer across the bow of the overtaking vessel.

2. As the overtaking vessel proceeds the length of time the two vessels will be subject to the low pressure areas along the sides of the vessel will be greater. Both vessels should be aware that the potential for both sterns being sucked towards each other is greater than when vessels are approaching head on.

3. When the bows are abeam of each other the positive pressure at the bow of each vessel causes the bows to be repelled.

4. As the overtaking vessel draws clear its rudder may be effected by the positive pressure at the bow of the vessel being overtaken causing it to sheer across the bow of the vessel being overtaken.

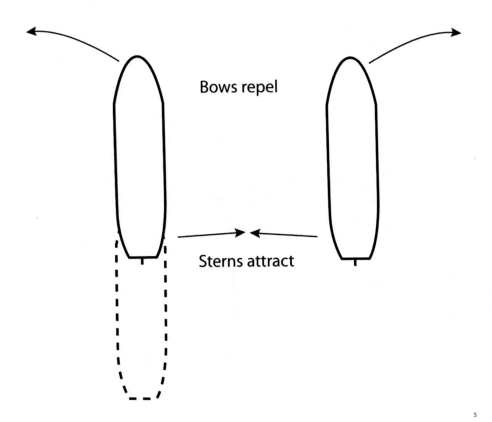

Bows repel

Sterns attract

5

---

5 Reproduced from *Seamanship Techniques, David House ref fig. 9.46*

KEY POINTS

♦ **The most critical effect is when the depth of water is less than twice the draught of the vessel.**

♦ **Reducing the ships speed reduces the effects of squat.**

As a vessel moves through the water, the greatest resistance is experienced at the bow. As the water is displaced, it moves faster under the bow of the vessel. This causes an area of low pressure at the bow and the reduction of buoyancy causes the bow to 'dip'.

The flow of water around the vessel will also increase in speed. The increase in water flow causes a reduction of water in the vicinity of the vessel. This fall in water level results in a loss of underkeel clearance known as 'squat'.

The resulting change of trim may render the rudder less effective and could result in the vessel taking a sudden sheer.

Factors Affecting Squat

- The speed of the vessel.
- Type of bow. This influences the bow wave produced and the distribution of pressure.
- Position of the longitudinal centre of buoyancy (LCB):
  - If the LCB is aft of midships, 'squat' by the stern should be expected.
  - If the LCB is forward of midships, 'squat' by the head should be expected.

Interaction – Use of Tugs

KEY POINTS

♦ Danger of the forward tug being overrun and capsizing.

♦ Danger of the aft tug experiencing damage from collision with the other vessel or from its propeller.

Taking a Line Forward

1. As the tug move forward it may be sucked into the vessels side due to the low-pressure area along the side of the vessel.

2. As the tug approaches the shoulder the positive pressure at the bow of the vessel pushes the bow of the tug away while the stern of the tug is sucked into the area of low pressure along the vessels side. The result is the tug shears away from the vessel.

3. The tug master applies helm to counteract this sheer. When the tug moves under the bow, the bow of the tug may not be affected by vessels positive pressure area. The stern of the tug may well be affected by this area pushing it away.

4. The end result being the tug takes a shear in front of the vessel and may be overrun.

Taking a Line Aft

1. Approaching a vessel from the stern, the tug master must increase power to overcome the positive pressure area astern of the vessel.

2. Once through the area of positive pressure, the tug will be affected by the low-pressure area which draws the tug towards the stern. The tug master must reduce power.

3. When moving alongside the vessel, the low-pressure area of the tug may be sucked into the area of low pressure long the vessel's side.

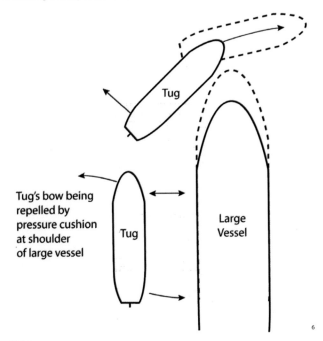

Tug

Tug's bow being repelled by pressure cushion at shoulder of large vessel

Tug

Large Vessel

6

---

6 Reproduced from Seamanship Techniques, David House ref fig. 9.48

For a right-handed screw propeller:

1. If the vessel is proceeding on the starboard side of the channel cross to port side. Turn will be made to starboard.

2. Once vessel is on port side of the channel, order half ahead and wheel hard to starboard. Once the vessel is seen to make headway, stop engine, wheel amidships.

3. Engines full astern. Effect of transverse thrust will swing the bow to starboard and the stern to port. Once the vessel is seen to make sternway, stop engine.

4. Engine half ahead and wheel hard to starboard. Vessel will continue its turn to starboard.

These actions are repeated until the vessel has completed her turn.

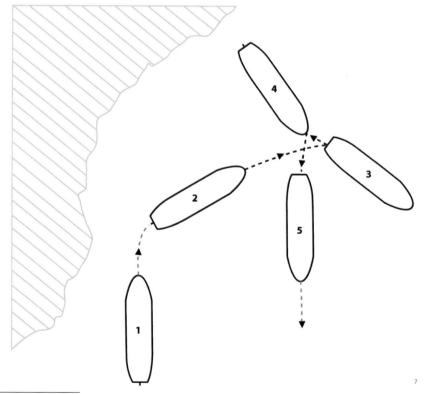

7

---

7 *Reproduced from Seamanship Techniques, David House ref fig. 9.38*

Response to
Emergencies

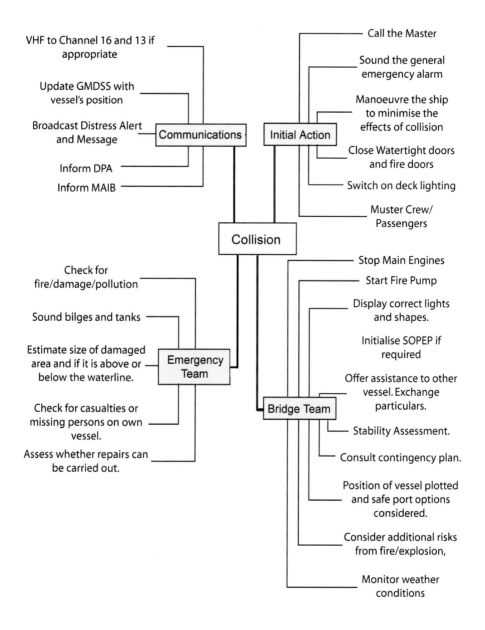

VHF to Channel 16 and 13 if appropriate

Update GMDSS with vessel's position

Broadcast Distress Alert and Message — **Communications**

Inform DPA

Inform MAIB

Initial Action

Call the Master

Sound the general emergency alarm

Manoeuvre the ship to minimise the effects of collision

Close Watertight doors and fire doors

Switch on deck lighting

Muster Crew/ Passengers

Collision

Check for fire/damage/pollution

Sound bilges and tanks

Estimate size of damaged area and if it is above or below the waterline. — **Emergency Team**

Check for casualties or missing persons on own vessel.

Assess whether repairs can be carried out.

Bridge Team

Stop Main Engines

Start Fire Pump

Display correct lights and shapes.

Initialise SOPEP if required

Offer assistance to other vessel. Exchange particulars.

Stability Assessment.

Consult contingency plan.

Position of vessel plotted and safe port options considered.

Consider additional risks from fire/explosion,

Monitor weather conditions

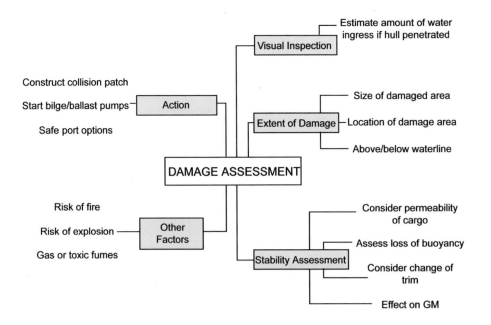

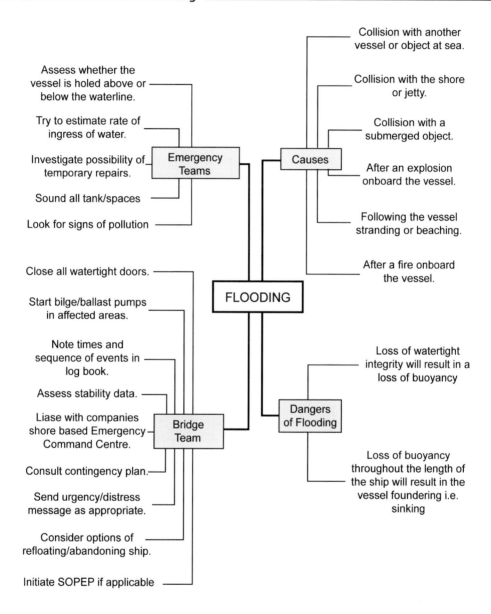

Collision with another vessel or object at sea.

Collision with the shore or jetty.

Collision with a submerged object.

After an explosion onboard the vessel.

Following the vessel stranding or beaching.

After a fire onboard the vessel.

Assess whether the vessel is holed above or below the waterline.

Try to estimate rate of ingress of water.

Investigate possibility of temporary repairs.

Sound all tank/spaces

Look for signs of pollution

Emergency Teams

Causes

FLOODING

Close all watertight doors.

Start bilge/ballast pumps in affected areas.

Note times and sequence of events in log book.

Assess stability data.

Liase with companies shore based Emergency Command Centre.

Consult contingency plan.

Send urgency/distress message as appropriate.

Consider options of refloating/abandoning ship.

Initiate SOPEP if applicable

Bridge Team

Dangers of Flooding

Loss of watertight integrity will result in a loss of buoyancy

Loss of buoyancy throughout the length of the ship will result in the vessel foundering i.e. sinking

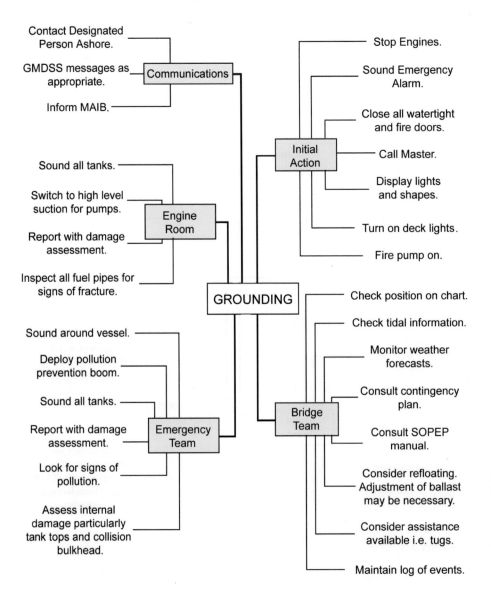

Contact Designated Person Ashore.

GMDSS messages as appropriate.

Inform MAIB.

Communications

Stop Engines.

Sound Emergency Alarm.

Close all watertight and fire doors.

Initial Action

Call Master.

Display lights and shapes.

Sound all tanks.

Switch to high level suction for pumps.

Report with damage assessment.

Engine Room

Turn on deck lights.

Fire pump on.

Inspect all fuel pipes for signs of fracture.

GROUNDING

Check position on chart.

Check tidal information.

Sound around vessel.

Deploy pollution prevention boom.

Sound all tanks.

Monitor weather forecasts.

Consult contingency plan.

Report with damage assessment.

Emergency Team

Bridge Team

Consult SOPEP manual.

Look for signs of pollution.

Consider refloating. Adjustment of ballast may be necessary.

Assess internal damage particularly tank tops and collision bulkhead.

Consider assistance available i.e. tugs.

Maintain log of events.

International Aeronautical and Maritime Search and Rescue Manual
Published jointly by IMO and the International Civil Aviation Organization (ICAO).

There are three volumes of the IAMSAR Manual and they provide guidelines for the co-ordination and organization of marine and air facilities in a search and rescue scenario.

Volume I Organization and Management

- Outlines the concept of a global search and rescue system.
- Discusses the need for the establishment and improvement of national and regional search and rescue systems.
- Discusses the need for co-operation between states in order to provide effective search and rescue services.

Volume II Mission Co-ordination

- This volume provides assistance to personnel who plan and co-ordinate search and rescue operations and exercises.

Volume III Mobile Facilities

- Carried onboard aircraft and ships.
- Mandatory for carriage onboard ships.
- Provides assistance in helping perform a search or rescue.
- Provides information on the role of on-scene co-ordinator.

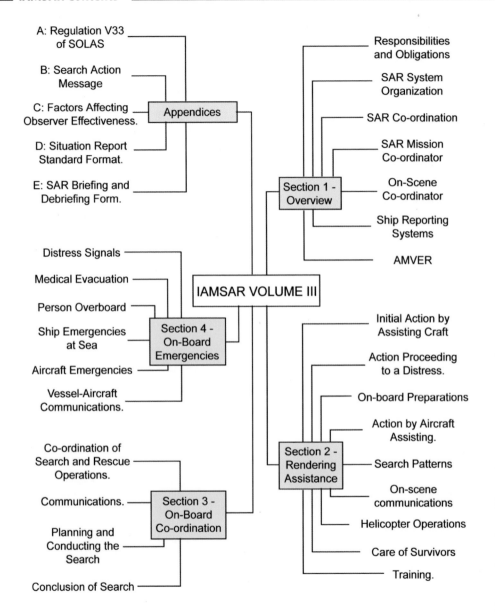

A: Regulation V33 of SOLAS

B: Search Action Message

C: Factors Affecting Observer Effectiveness.

D: Situation Report Standard Format.

E: SAR Briefing and Debriefing Form.

Appendices

Responsibilities and Obligations

SAR System Organization

SAR Co-ordination

SAR Mission Co-ordinator

On-Scene Co-ordinator

Ship Reporting Systems

AMVER

Section 1 - Overview

Distress Signals

Medical Evacuation

Person Overboard

Ship Emergencies at Sea

Aircraft Emergencies

Vessel-Aircraft Communications.

Section 4 - On-Board Emergencies

IAMSAR VOLUME III

Initial Action by Assisting Craft

Action Proceeding to a Distress.

On-board Preparations

Action by Aircraft Assisting.

Search Patterns

On-scene communications

Helicopter Operations

Care of Survivors

Training.

Section 2 - Rendering Assistance

Co-ordination of Search and Rescue Operations.

Communications.

Planning and Conducting the Search

Conclusion of Search

Section 3 - On-Board Co-ordination

Content of Fire Wallet

- Up to date stability information.
- Up to date crew list.
- Plans of the vessel e.g. General Arrangement, Life Saving Appliances, Ventilation.
- Copy of ship contingency plans.
- Copy of emergency contact details.
- Copy of ventilation fire flap shut off points.
- Cargo plan and dangerous goods plan

Information to Hand Over to Fire Crew

- Location of fire and how to get access it.
- Briefing of spaces in the vicinity of fire, contents and risks involved.
- Any action that has already been taken i.e. ventilation shut down, machinery isolated, boundary cooling in operation.
- Any persons unaccounted for.
- Establish communications system.
- Current stability information and status of fuel, ballast and fresh water tanks.

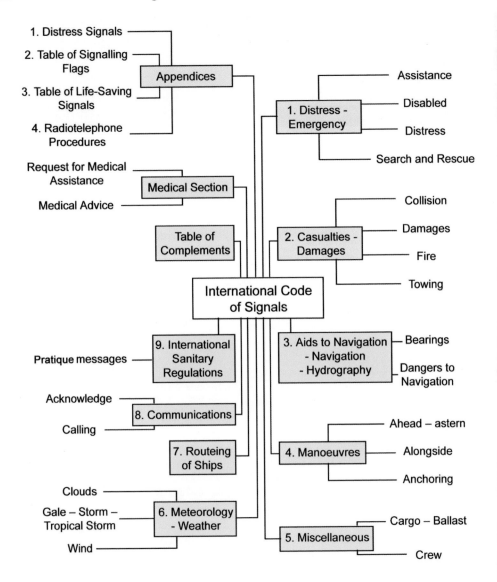

1. Distress Signals
2. Table of Signalling Flags
3. Table of Life-Saving Signals
4. Radiotelephone Procedures

Appendices

Request for Medical Assistance
Medical Advice

Medical Section

Table of Complements

International Code of Signals

1. Distress - Emergency
- Assistance
- Disabled
- Distress
- Search and Rescue

2. Casualties - Damages
- Collision
- Damages
- Fire
- Towing

3. Aids to Navigation - Navigation - Hydrography
- Bearings
- Dangers to Navigation

9. International Sanitary Regulations
- Pratique messages

8. Communications
- Acknowledge
- Calling

7. Routeing of Ships

4. Manoeuvres
- Ahead – astern
- Alongside
- Anchoring

6. Meteorology - Weather
- Clouds
- Gale – Storm – Tropical Storm
- Wind

5. Miscellaneous
- Cargo – Ballast
- Crew

Organisation of Fire Parties and Drills

Emergency Party
Fire Control Station
C/O, Bosun
Excellent local knowledge

Engine Room Party
Engine Control Room
2nd Eng, ETO
Excellent local knowledge

Command Party
On Bridge
Master, Chief Engineer
Decision Makers

First Aid Party
Hospital
Qualified in first aid

Back Up Party
Prepare lifeboats / boundary
cooling. Knowledge of LSA & FFA
equipment.

Organisation of fire parties depends on size/experience of crew and type of vessel.

Emergency Drills
- Should be as realistic as possible and involve everybody.
- Should be held in conjunction with first stage of an abandon ship drill.
- At least one fire extinguisher should be released per drill.

Party	Tasks During a Drill
Emergency Party	- BA suits and fire suits on. - Everyone familiar with fire extinguishing appliances. - Testing of fixed fire installations as realistically as possible.
Engine Room Party	- Operate fire pumps. - Operate emergency fire pump.
Back Up Party	- Close ventilation fire flaps. - Knowledge of remote controls for emergency stops for vent fans, fuel oil pumps and oil tank valves.
First Aid Party	- Familiarisation with first aid equipment and techniques.

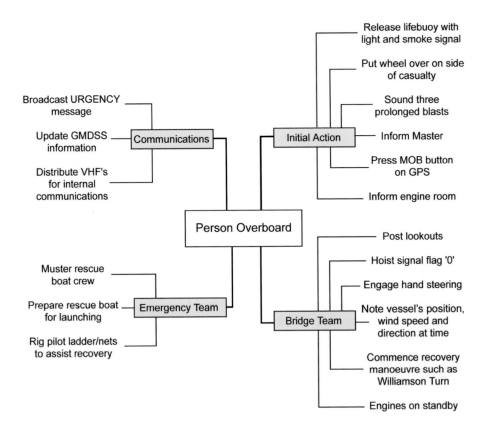

Broadcast URGENCY message

Update GMDSS information

Distribute VHF's for internal communications

Communications

Release lifebuoy with light and smoke signal

Put wheel over on side of casualty

Sound three prolonged blasts

Initial Action

Inform Master

Press MOB button on GPS

Inform engine room

Person Overboard

Muster rescue boat crew

Prepare rescue boat for launching

Rig pilot ladder/nets to assist recovery

Emergency Team

Post lookouts

Hoist signal flag 'O'

Engage hand steering

Bridge Team

Note vessel's position, wind speed and direction at time

Commence recovery manoeuvre such as Williamson Turn

Engines on standby

Single Turn

Advantages: In an immediate action situation will bring the vessel round in the quickest time.

Disadvantages: Does not bring the vessel round into its own wake so not effective for a delayed action or a person-missing situation.

1. Rudder hard over to the side of the casualty.
2. Deviate 250° from the original course.
3. Rudder amidships. Stop vessel.
4. Maintain speed throughout turn

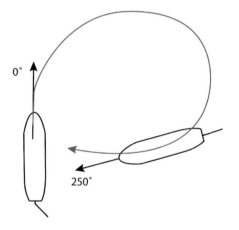

Williamson Turn

Advantages: After the turn has been completed the vessel will be proceeding on a reciprocal course in its own wake. Can be used for any situation.

Disadvantages: Not as quick as the single turn in an immediate action situation.

1. Rudder hard over to the side of the casualty.
2. Deviate 60° from original course. Put rudder hard over to the opposite side.
3. When 20° from reciprocal course rudder amidships and steady up on reciprocal.

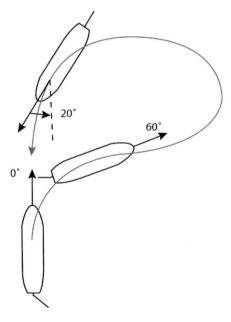

Scharnow Turn

Advantages: After the turn has been completed the vessel will be proceeding on a reciprocal course in its own wake. In a person missing situation the Scharnow Turn will bring the vessel round in a quicker time

Disadvantages: Not to be used in an immediate action as the vessel will complete its turn astern of the start of turn position therefore leaving an area unsearched.

1. Rudder hard over.
2. Deviate 240° from original course.
3. Rudder hard over to opposite side.
4. When heading is 20° from reciprocal course rudder amidships and steady up on reciprocal.

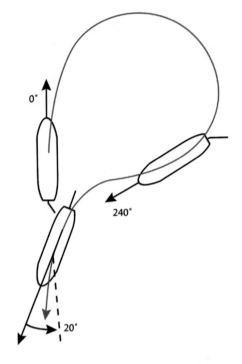

Proceeding to a Distress

Immediate Action

If the vessel is able to assist in a distress. Acknowledge receipt of the distress, establish R/T communications and get the following information from the vessel in distress:

- Position and nature of the distress.
- Distressed vessel's identity, call sign, name and number of people on board.
- What type of assistance is required and number of casualties if any.
- Distressed vessel's course and speed.
- Type of cargo carried.
- Any other information relevant to the rescue.

Proceeding to the Area of Distress

- Establish communications with CRS (Coast Radio Station) and SMC (Search and Rescue Mission Co-ordinator) as well as other traffic proceeding to distress.
- Continue systematic plotting of all vessels in the area.
- Update own vessel's ETA to distress site and note the ETA's of other vessel's proceeding to the distress site.
- Monitor the situation in preparation for arriving at the scene.
- Consult IAMSAR Vol. III and company procedures.

Onboard Preparations

While proceeding to the distress the following LSA gear should be prepared.

- Rescue boat, lifeboat.
- Lifejackets, immersion suits.
- Portable VHF radios.
- Lifebuoys, buoyant lifelines.
- Pilot ladder, scrambling nets.
- International Code of Signals.
- Line throwing apparatus.
- GMDSS equipment manned.
- Fire fighting equipment.
- Binoculars, extra lookouts.
- Search lights, signal lamps and torches.
- Pyrotechnics.
- Stretcher, medical supplies and medicines.

Protection of Passengers

KEY POINTS

♦ Class I, II and IIA passenger ships are required to have a decision support system for the emergency management of the ship.

♦ This system identifies all foreseeable emergency situations and details the procedures that should take place.

♦ The plans can be kept in paper or electronic format.

Emergency Information for Passengers

Signs

- Muster station signs should be prominent. They should be readily visible to passengers and clearly identify the muster station.

- The routes leading to passenger muster stations should also be clearly marked. These markings will be in passenger cabins, alleyways and stairways leading to the muster stations.

- 'Exit' signs should be displayed on doors from passenger spaces leading to open decks.

- All emergency exit routes should be signposted.

- Each deck clearly labelled and 'you are here' maps prominent.

Passenger Emergency Instruction Notes

- Available in passenger cabins, muster stations and passenger spaces these give information on where to muster, how to don a lifejacket and action in the event of an emergency.

Public Address Systems

- Should be capable of being heard in all public spaces including open decks.

Passenger Emergency Instructions

- The attention of the passengers should be drawn to emergency information by means of a public address prior to, or immediately after the vessel has sailed. Any public address should be preceded by a special signal in order to attract the publics' attention.

Reference:
MSN 1409 Emergency Information for Passengers
MSN 1386 Emergency Information for Passengers Class 3, 4, 5,6 and 6A
MGN 71 Musters, Drills and Decision Making

International Convention on Oil Pollution Preparedness, response and Co-operation 1990

- Ships required to carry shipboard oil pollution emergency plan.
- Ships required to report incidents of pollution to coastal authorities.
- Establishment of stockpiles of oil spill combating equipment.
- Requirement for oil spill combating exercises.
- Development of detailed plans dealing with pollution incidents.

Responsibility

- In the UK the Maritime and Coastguard Agency (MCA) is responsible for responding to pollution from shipping and offshore installations.
- 'The National Contingency Plan for Marine Pollution from Shipping and Offshore Installations' published in 2000 details command and control procedures to deal with an incident.
- Procedures are in place to deal with any emergency at sea that causes pollution or threatens to cause pollution.

Counter Pollution and Response

- Formerly the Marine Pollution Control Unit, this is a branch of the MCA providing a command and control structure to assist decision-making in an emergency.

- Each MCA region has a Counter Pollution and Salvage Officer whose task is to decide the relevant course of action in the event of a threat to the marine environment by a ship drifting or aground.
- In the event of a major event the Marine Emergency Information room may be activated in Southampton.

Tier System of Spills

Tier One – Small Operational spill. Local resources required during clear up.

Tier two – Medium sized spill. Requires regional equipment and resources.

Tier Three – Large spill. Requires national assistance and resources.

Reporting of Incidents

Masters must report any of the following:

- Any accident where oil spills or spill of harmful substances occurs.
- An observation of a spill of oil or harmful substances, which occurs at sea.
- The report should be made to HM Coastguard if in UK waters or to the nearest coastal state if outside UK waters.

Search and Rescue in the UK

HM Coastguard responsible for search and rescue operations in the UK.

- Split into 3 regions. Each region has Maritime Rescue Co-ordination Centres (MRCC)
- Foreign Search and Rescue Regions (SRR) have a UK liaison station.
- Details of worldwide search and rescue regions contained in Admiralty List of Radio Signals Volume 5.

Once a distress has bee initialised the MRCC will act as the Search and Rescue Mission Co-ordinator (SMC) whose duties will include.

- Responsible for the search and rescue.
- Responsible for allocating resources.
- SMCs appoint an On Scene Co-ordinator.
- SMC gathers all current and future weather information.
- Initiate broadcasts through VHF, MF, HF, Navtex, Satcoms as appropriate.
- Ensure good communications throughout.
- Liase with media.

If more than one unit is being used in a rescue the SMC will normally appoint an On-Scene Co-ordinator. The OSC will be a marine unit with excellent communications such as a passenger vessel. Their duties will include.

- Receiving instruction from the SMC.
- Co-ordinate the units involved in the search and issue them instructions.
- Informing the SMC of any modifications to the search plan if appropriate.
- Inform the SMC when units arrive or leave the search and whether any additional units are required.

Search Patterns

Establishing a Datum

Factors to be considered

- Last reported position and time of distress.
- Time interval between the last report and the arrival of SAR facilities.
- An estimate of how the distressed craft will move over the water surface. This is known as drift and there are two items to consider.
  1. Leeway, the craft will move downwind dependent on the wind speed.
  2. Total water current, an estimate of the set and drift at the scene.
- The datum position is found by plotting the last known position and applying the direction of drift and speed of drift.

Establishing a Search Pattern

Track spacing

- A table of recommended track spacing for merchant vessels is given in IAMSAR Volume III. These are dependent on the object in the water and the meteorological visibility.
- Track spacing should be altered if there is a change in the visibility or the number of vessels taking part in the search.
- It is the responsibility of the SMC to ensure that there is a safe spacing between all ships and aircraft involved in the search and that the required search pattern is being conducted effectively.

Search Patterns

Expanding Square Search	Where search will be conducted over a relatively small area. Search conducted by one vessel starting at datum.
Sector Search	Best when datum is accurate and search area small.
	Conducted by single vessel. Marker may be dropped at datum to be used as a reference.
	Aircraft and vessel may perform independent sector searches of the same area.
Creeping Line Search	Performed when aircraft or vessel has disappeared along a known route.
Parallel Sweep Search	Used to search large area where search location is uncertain. Search legs are parallel to each other. May be carried out by multiple vessels.

Creeping Line Search

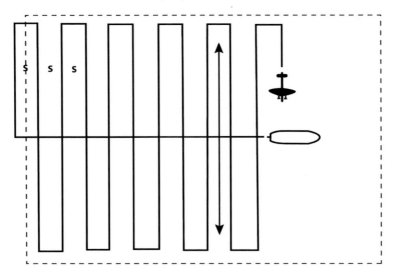

Expanding Square Search

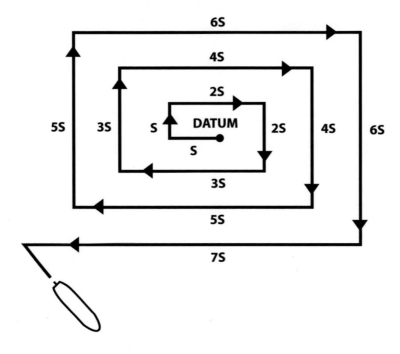

Parallel Search 2 and 3 Ships

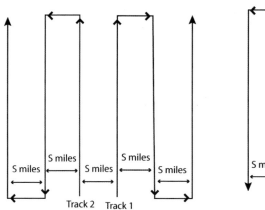

S miles S miles S miles S miles

Track 2   Track 1

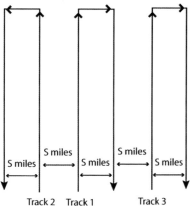

S miles S miles S miles S miles

Track 2   Track 1   Track 3

Parallel Search 5 Ships

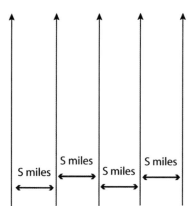

S miles   S miles   S miles   S miles

6 etc. - Track 4   Track 2   Track 1   Track 3   Track 5 - 7 etc.

Emergency Towing Arrangements

Aft Emergency Towing Arrangements

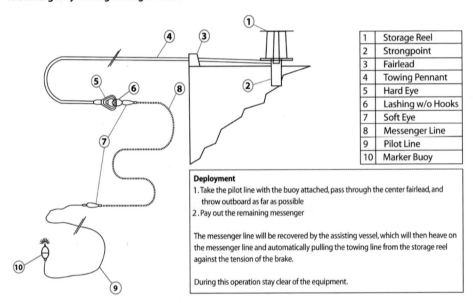

1	Storage Reel
2	Strongpoint
3	Fairlead
4	Towing Pennant
5	Hard Eye
6	Lashing w/o Hooks
7	Soft Eye
8	Messenger Line
9	Pilot Line
10	Marker Buoy

Deployment

1. Take the pilot line with the buoy attached, pass through the center fairlead, and throw outboard as far as possible
2. Pay out the remaining messenger

The messenger line will be recovered by the assisting vessel, which will then heave on the messenger line and automatically pulling the towing line from the storage reel against the tension of the brake.

During this operation stay clear of the equipment.

Receipt of a Distress Message

Own Vessel is in	DISTRESS RECEIVED ON		
	VHF Ch 70	MF 2187.5 kHz	Any HF Band
Area 1	1	5	3
Area 2	4	2	3
Area 3	4	5	3

1	2	3	4	5
a) Tune to Ch 16 and listen for distress communications.	a) Tune to 2182kHz and listen for distress comms.	a) Tune to R/T distress frequency on which distress alert was received.	a) Tune to Ch 16 and listen for distress communications	a) Tune to 2182kHz and listen for distress comms.
b) Ack. receipt on R/T Ch16. Carry out distress comms.	b) Ack. receipt on R/T 2182kHZ and carry out distress comms.	b) Do NOT ack. by R/T or DSC.	b) Ack. receipt on R/T Ch16. Carry out distress comms	b) Ack. receipt on R/T 2182kHZ and carry out distress comms.
c) If no response by shore station ack. On DSC ch 70 and relay distress ashore.	c) If no response by shore station ack. on DSC 2187.5kHZ and relay distress ashore.	c) Wait at least 3 mins for shore to send ack.	c) If alert continues relay ashore using any available means.	c) If alert continues relay ashore using any available means
		d) If no shore ack. and no distress R/T heard, relay alert ashore.	d) Ack. alert by DSC on Ch 70.	d) Ack. alert by DSC 2187.5kHz.
		e) If in VHF or MF range of distress try to contact on Ch16 or 2182kHz.		

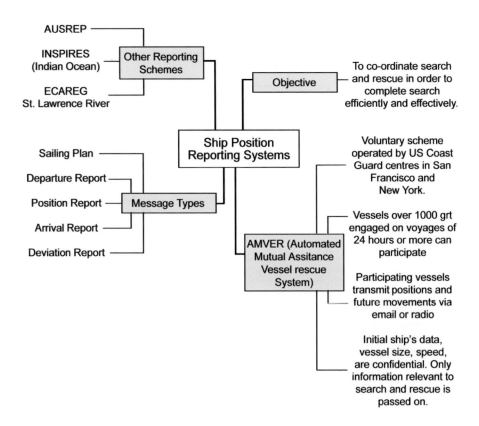

AUSREP

INSPIRES
(Indian Ocean) — Other Reporting Schemes

ECAREG
St. Lawrence River

Objective — To co-ordinate search and rescue in order to complete search efficiently and effectively.

Ship Position Reporting Systems

Sailing Plan

Departure Report

Position Report — Message Types

Arrival Report

Deviation Report

AMVER (Automated Mutual Assitance Vessel rescue System)

Voluntary scheme operated by US Coast Guard centres in San Francisco and New York.

Vessels over 1000 grt engaged on voyages of 24 hours or more can participate

Participating vessels transmit positions and future movements via email or radio

Initial ship's data, vessel size, speed, are confidential. Only information relevant to search and rescue is passed on.

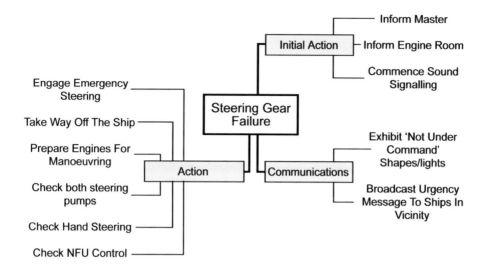

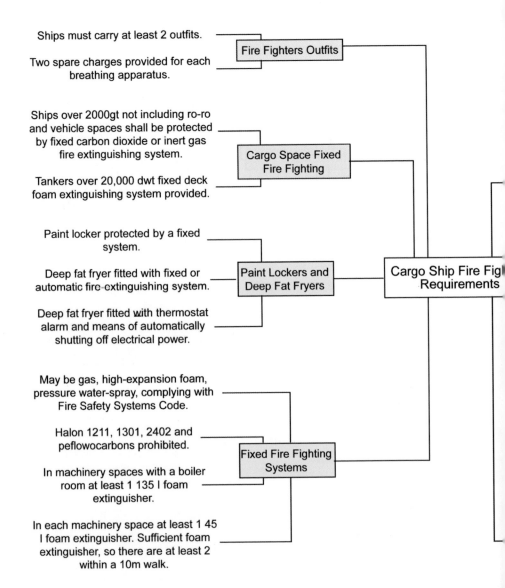

Ships must carry at least 2 outfits.

Two spare charges provided for each breathing apparatus.

Fire Fighters Outfits

Ships over 2000gt not including ro-ro and vehicle spaces shall be protected by fixed carbon dioxide or inert gas fire extinguishing system.

Tankers over 20,000 dwt fixed deck foam extinguishing system provided.

Cargo Space Fixed Fire Fighting

Paint locker protected by a fixed system.

Deep fat fryer fitted with fixed or automatic fire-extinguishing system.

Deep fat fryer fitted with thermostat alarm and means of automatically shutting off electrical power.

Paint Lockers and Deep Fat Fryers

May be gas, high-expansion foam, pressure water-spray, complying with Fire Safety Systems Code.

Halon 1211, 1301, 2402 and peflowocarbons prohibited.

In machinery spaces with a boiler room at least 1 135 l foam extinguisher.

In each machinery space at least 1 45 l foam extinguisher. Sufficient foam extinguisher, so there are at least 2 within a 10m walk.

Fixed Fire Fighting Systems

Cargo Ship Fire Fig Requirements

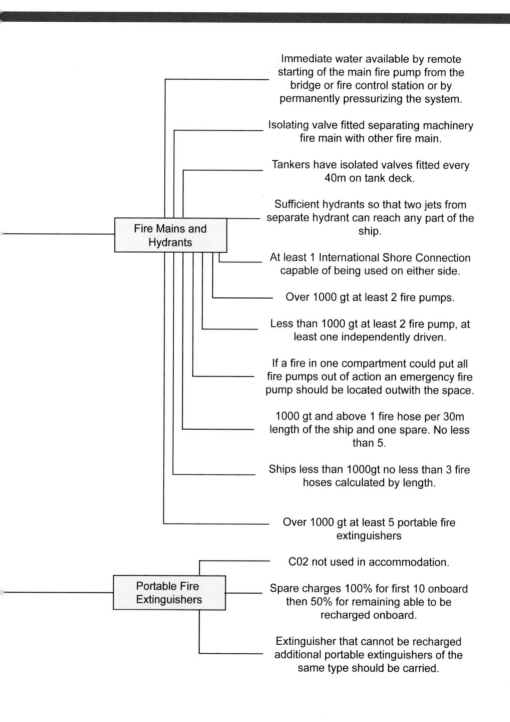

Fire Mains and Hydrants

- Immediate water available by remote starting of the main fire pump from the bridge or fire control station or by permanently pressurizing the system.

- Isolating valve fitted separating machinery fire main with other fire main.

- Tankers have isolated valves fitted every 40m on tank deck.

- Sufficient hydrants so that two jets from separate hydrant can reach any part of the ship.

- At least 1 International Shore Connection capable of being used on either side.

- Over 1000 gt at least 2 fire pumps.

- Less than 1000 gt at least 2 fire pump, at least one independently driven.

- If a fire in one compartment could put all fire pumps out of action an emergency fire pump should be located outwith the space.

- 1000 gt and above 1 fire hose per 30m length of the ship and one spare. No less than 5.

- Ships less than 1000gt no less than 3 fire hoses calculated by length.

- Over 1000 gt at least 5 portable fire extinguishers

Portable Fire Extinguishers

- C02 not used in accommodation.

- Spare charges 100% for first 10 onboard then 50% for remaining able to be recharged onboard.

- Extinguisher that cannot be recharged additional portable extinguishers of the same type should be carried.

Care of Fire Fighting Appliances

FFA Maintenance and Inspection

All maintenance should be recorded as part of
the planned maintenance system, in line with
the SMS.

Monthly	· Check fire suits, fire extinguishers, nozzles, hydrants, hoses and nozzles are all in place and ready for use. · All escape routes, doorways and stairways are accessible. · The ships alarms and public address system are functioning. · The fixed fire fighting system is checked and available if required. · Sprinkler system is operational and pressurised. · Fire pumps are operational.
Quarterly	· Fire extinguisher is within service date and is at correct pressure. · International shore connection is checked and serviceable. · Full inventory of fire fighting equipment lockers. · Fire doors, fire dampers and closing devices are checked and can be operated locally.
Annually	· All fire doors and ventilation dampers can operate remotely. · Check water and foam fixed fire-fighting installations are operating correctly. · Fire pumps work at correct pressure and flow rates. · All hydrants operational. · Cross connection between fire main and sprinkler valve operate correctly. · Fixed fire fighting equipment tested as per manufacturers instructions.

Reference:
MGN 71 Musters drills and decision making

Portable Fire Extinguishers

Type of Portable Extinguisher	Basic Service	Extended Service (Test Discharge)	Overhaul (Hydraulic Test)
Water, foam and water based	Every Year	Every 5 Years	Every 10 Years
Powder	Every Year	Every 10 Years	Every 10 Years
Powder Primary Sealed	Every Year	Every 10 Years (Returned to manufacturer/supplier for recharge)	Every 10 Years
CO_2	Every Year	Every 5 Years	Every 10 Years

- Basic and extended services may be carried out onboard ship as part of the planned maintenance system.

- These services must be under the supervision of a competent person. A competent person is someone who holds a Merchant Shipping STCW II/2 or unlimited III/2 certificate of competency and an Advanced Fire Fighting Certificate.

- During these services all procedures, work instructions and tools to be readily available. Any plastic collars, which may conceal the condition of the cylinder underneath, must be removed to enable a complete inspection.

- After inspection each extinguisher must have a maintenance label indicating a competent person has examined it on a certain date.

Reference:
MGN 71 (M) Musters, Drills and Decision Making

Initial Action	• Raise the alarm.
	• Identify location.
	• Start fire pump.
	• Muster personnel.
	• Establish communications with emergency parties.
	• Close fire and watertight doors.
	• Isolate electrical circuits in the vicinity of the fire.
	• Send BA teams to tackle fire.
	• Commence boundary cooling.
	• Follow ship's contingency plans.
	• Broadcast GMDSS emergency message.
	• Stop fans/ventilation to the area.
	• If the fire is discovered at a very early stage have one attempt to extinguish the fire and raise the alarm.
Accommodation Fires	• Potential hazards: waste paper baskets, furnishings.
	• Establish the class of fire and use the appropriate extinguisher.
	• Remove furnishings from adjacent cabins and commence boundary cooling.
Galley Fires	• Potential hazards: oil and fat in pans, heat off the galley
	• Close off ventilation to the galley.
	• Additional fire appliances (which may be available in the galley): fire blanket, foam extinguishers, fixed fire-fighting appliances above the galley range.
Machinery Space	• Potential hazards: oil spills, fuel oil leaks.
	• Extra foam extinguishers are available to tackle fires.
	• Fixed fire-fighting systems are fitted to engine rooms in case the fire gets out of control.

Classes and Chemistry of Fire

Combustion will take place when three items react:

1) Fuel
2) An ignition Source
3) Oxygen

Remove one of these three factors and combustion will not take place.

The Fire Triangle

Classes of Fire	
Class A	Carbonaceous
Class B	Liquids and Liquefiable solids
Class C	Gases and Liquefiable gases
Class D	Metals
Electricity itself does not burn. Remove the source of electricity and identify the class of fire before using appropriate methods of extinguishing.	

Portable Fire Extinguishers						
Type	**Purpose**	**Colour Band**	**Duration**	**Throw**	**Advantages**	**Disadvantages**
Water	Class 'A'	Signal Red	1 minute	6 metres	Excellent cooling effect.	Conducts electricity. May damage cargo.
Foam	Class 'B'	Pale Cream	1 minute	4 metres	Smothers fire reducing possibility of re-ignition.	Conducts electricity. Messy.
AFFF (Aqueous Film Forming Foam)	Class 'A' Class 'B'	Pale Cream	1 minute	4 metres	Used for flammable liquids. 5 times more effective than foam.	Breaks down easily.
CO_2	Class 'B' Class 'C' Electricity	Black or Red with black band	30 secs	2 metres	Can be used on electrical fires. Does not damage equipment.	Can cause freeze burns. Dense vapour may hinder visibility. Very noisy when operated. Can be toxic.
Dry Powder	Class 'A' Class 'B' Class 'C' Electricity	Blue	25 secs (approx)	4 metres	Can be used on most fires. Does not conduct electricity.	Powder can compact in the cylinder. Leaves a residue. Does not cool.

Emergency Escape Breathing Devices

- Used to escape from control stations, machinery spaces, accommodation spaces and service area in the event of an emergency.

- All ships must carry at least two emergency escape breathing devices (EEBD) in the accommodation - and one spare.

- Passenger ships carrying more than 36 passengers should carry at least four EEBDs in every main vertical zone - and two spare.

- In machinery spaces, EEBDs should be clearly visible.

- Use EEBDs to escape from a compartment.

- EEBDs have a service duration of at least 10 minutes.

- A full set of EEBD includes a hood or full-face piece. (Gives protection to the eyes nose and mouth during escape.)

Self Contained Breathing Apparatus

- Each set should include an attachment for an alternative air supply to be connected to the apparatus.

- Storage capacity of the cylinder shall be at least 1,200 litres of fresh air.

- The air delivered to the user should be regulated as to his/her requirements. An override should allow the volume of air pressure to be increased as required.

- Each set should be fitted with an anti-burst pressure gauge to allow the wearer to read the pressure of air in the cylinder.

- Every set of breathing apparatus should have spare cylinders to provide a total capacity of 2,400 litres of air. Exceptions:

  - If a ship carries 5 or more sets, the total spare capacity need not exceed 9,600 litres.

  - If the ship carries a breathing-apparatus air compressor which can re-charge cylinders, each set may have a spare cylinder capacity of 1,200 litres with the total spare storage air capacity of 4,800 litres.

- Each set of breathing apparatus should have it own servicing and instruction manual.

- Every set should also contain:

  - A fireproof life and signalling line.

  - Adjustable safety belt or harness.

  - Means of smoke-protection for the eyes and face of the wearer.

  - Non-flammable plates containing code of signals to be used between the wearer and his/her attendant.

Reference:
MSN 1665 The Merchant Shipping (Fire Protection) Regulations.

Fire and Safety Plans

KEY POINTS

♦ In the event of an emergency, all crew should have the knowledge required to tackle a fire efficiently.

♦ To gain this knowledge, use regular training and drills and practice with the LSA and FFA equipment carried onboard the vessel.

Fire control plans are permanently exhibited at various locations. These plans show a breakdown of the vessel, deck by deck, and where the fixed and portable FFA and LSA can be found in each section. These plans include:

- Location of all control stations.
- Sections enclosed by 'A' class divisions.
- Sections enclosed by 'B' class divisions.
- Fire detection and fire alarm systems.
- Sprinkler system - if applicable.
- Location of portable and fixed fire-fighting appliances.
- Fan control positions for the ventilation system.
- Position of the dampers and the identification number for the ventilation fans in each section.

Provide this information in booklet form and give one to each officer. Make provision for additional booklets to be readily-accessible on the ship.

Record all alterations to plans or booklets as soon as possible.

Provide a copy of the plan or booklet in the working language of the ship. If this is not English or French, provide a translation.

To assist shore-side fire fighters in the event of an emergency, place a copy of the fire control plans in a weathertight container at the gangway.

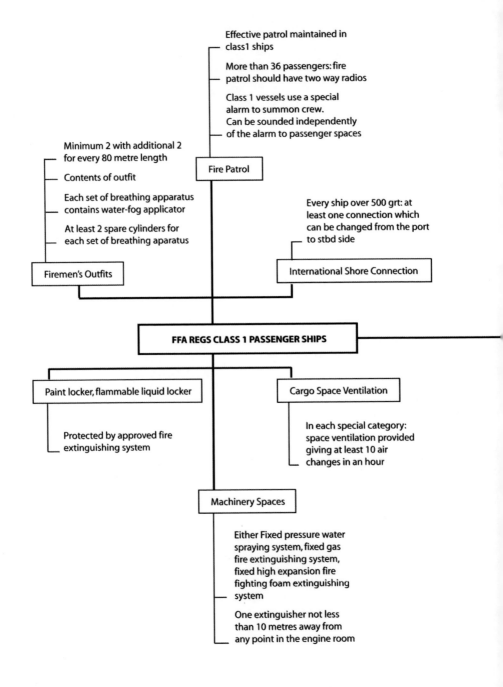

Effective patrol maintained in class1 ships

More than 36 passengers: fire patrol should have two way radios

Class 1 vessels use a special alarm to summon crew. Can be sounded independently of the alarm to passenger spaces

Fire Patrol

Minimum 2 with additional 2 for every 80 metre length

Contents of outfit

Each set of breathing apparatus contains water-fog applicator

At least 2 spare cylinders for each set of breathing aparatus

Firemen's Outfits

Every ship over 500 grt: at least one connection which can be changed from the port to stbd side

International Shore Connection

FFA REGS CLASS 1 PASSENGER SHIPS

Paint locker, flammable liquid locker

Protected by approved fire extinguishing system

Cargo Space Ventilation

In each special category: space ventilation provided giving at least 10 air changes in an hour

Machinery Spaces

Either Fixed pressure water spraying system, fixed gas fire extinguishing system, fixed high expansion fire fighting foam extinguishing system

One extinguisher not less than 10 metres away from any point in the engine room

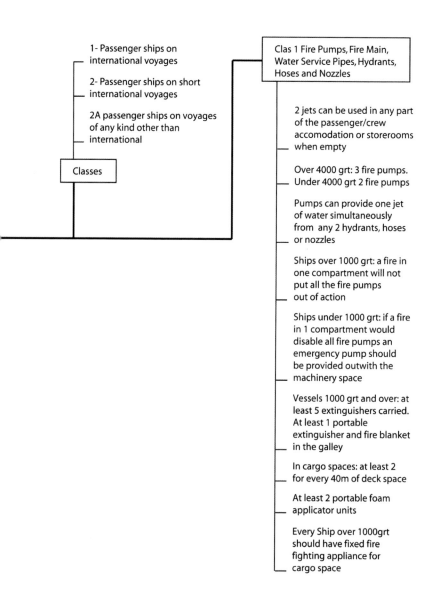

1- Passenger ships on international voyages

2- Passenger ships on short international voyages

2A passenger ships on voyages of any kind other than international

Classes

Clas 1 Fire Pumps, Fire Main, Water Service Pipes, Hydrants, Hoses and Nozzles

2 jets can be used in any part of the passenger/crew accomodation or storerooms when empty

Over 4000 grt: 3 fire pumps. Under 4000 grt 2 fire pumps

Pumps can provide one jet of water simultaneously from any 2 hydrants, hoses or nozzles

Ships over 1000 grt: a fire in one compartment will not put all the fire pumps out of action

Ships under 1000 grt: if a fire in 1 compartment would disable all fire pumps an emergency pump should be provided outwith the machinery space

Vessels 1000 grt and over: at least 5 extinguishers carried. At least 1 portable extinguisher and fire blanket in the galley

In cargo spaces: at least 2 for every 40m of deck space

At least 2 portable foam applicator units

Every Ship over 1000grt should have fixed fire fighting appliance for cargo space

Checks Before Use

Apparatus Leak Test

- Switch off the demand valve.
- Open the cylinder valve slowly, close it and observe the gauge. It should not fall more than 10 bar per minute.

Test the Whistle

- Release the pressure in the apparatus slowly, then open the demand valve switch. For a 1,200 litre cylinder, whistle should sound at 68 bar.

Don the Apparatus

- Check all straps are in good condition. Tighten the straps so the cylinder fits snugly on the back. The facemask should hang around the neck.
- With the demand valve off, turn on the cylinder slowly

Check for Positive Pressure

- Put the facemask on. Turn the demand valve on.
- Lift the mask seal off the face; air pressure should flow out of the mask. This proves there is positive pressure.
- Allow the mask to re-seal. Hold breath; check there is no leakage from the exhale valve.
- There should be a constant flow of air from the demand valve.

Check Face Mask for Leakage

- Close the cylinder valve and breathe until the facemask is drawn into the face. When the pressure gauge reads zero, hold breath for 10 seconds. If there is no leakage, the mask will continue to be drawn close to the face. If a leak is detected, open cylinder valve and re-adjust head straps.

Check the Actual Pressure Gauge

- Turn the cylinder on fully and check the reading on the pressure gauge.

Shutdown and Isolation of Equipment

Ventilation

- The main inlet and outlet valves used to ventilate a space should be capable of being shut down from outside the space. Mark the means of closing with a positive OPEN/CLOSED indication for the shut-off.

- For accommodation spaces, service spaces, control stations and machinery spaces, the power ventilation should be stopped from a location outside of these spaces. The location of the 'stops' should not be easily cut off by the fire.

Machinery Spaces

- Skylights, ventilator dampers, openings in funnels require a means of closure that is located outside space they serve.

- Ventilation fans serving the machinery spaces shall be capable of being stopped from two locations: one location should be outside the machinery space. The means for stopping machinery ventilation should be independent of the means of stopping ventilation to any other part of the ship.

- 'Stops' for draught fans, oil fuel transfer pumps, oil fuel unit pumps, lubricating oil service pumps purifiers and thermal oil circulating pumps should be located outside the space to enable access to them in the event of fire.

The Fire Main

- An isolating valve should be fitted to separate the machinery fire pump and fire main with the rest of the ship.

- With the fire main isolation valve shut, all hydrants on the ship can be supplied with water from the emergency fire pump or another fire pump located outside the machinery space.

Contents of SOLAS Manual

KEY POINTS

- Contains instructions and information on the life-saving appliances carried by the ship.
- Details personal protective equipment carried and its location.
- Gives information on survival at sea, hazards of exposure.
- Methods of launch and recovery of survival craft.
- Information on how to carry out emergency repairs on life-saving appliances.

- The SOLAS training manual may reproduce some information already contained in shipboard emergency plans.
- The SOLAS training manual provides reference information for officers who provide training to the crew. It is also a useful source of reference for the crew.
- In ships over 500 gt, a copy must be provided in the recreation or messroom.
- Provide copies of this manual in the working language of the ship.
- Provide onboard instruction in the use of LSA and FFA equipment when ship-specific training in these areas is not possible. Devise a programme of instruction to cover all parts of the LSA and FFA equipment in a two-month period.

References:
MGN 71 (M) Musters Drills and Decision Making

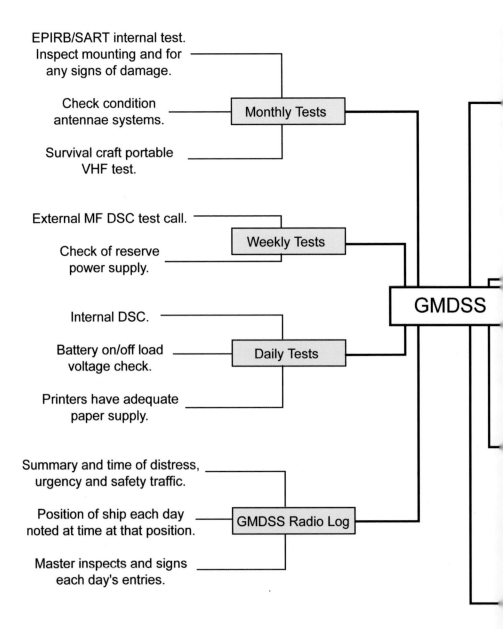

EPIRB/SART internal test. Inspect mounting and for any signs of damage.

Check condition antennae systems.

Survival craft portable VHF test.

Monthly Tests

External MF DSC test call.

Check of reserve power supply.

Weekly Tests

Internal DSC.

Battery on/off load voltage check.

Printers have adequate paper supply.

Daily Tests

Summary and time of distress, urgency and safety traffic.

Position of ship each day noted at time at that position.

Master inspects and signs each day's entries.

GMDSS Radio Log

GMDSS

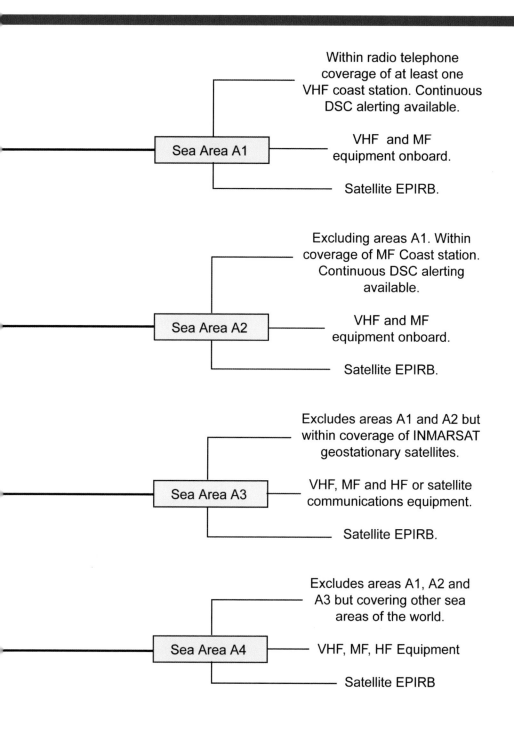

Sea Area A1
- Within radio telephone coverage of at least one VHF coast station. Continuous DSC alerting available.
- VHF and MF equipment onboard.
- Satellite EPIRB.

Sea Area A2
- Excluding areas A1. Within coverage of MF Coast station. Continuous DSC alerting available.
- VHF and MF equipment onboard.
- Satellite EPIRB.

Sea Area A3
- Excludes areas A1 and A2 but within coverage of INMARSAT geostationary satellites.
- VHF, MF and HF or satellite communications equipment.
- Satellite EPIRB.

Sea Area A4
- Excludes areas A1, A2 and A3 but covering other sea areas of the world.
- VHF, MF, HF Equipment
- Satellite EPIRB

KEY POINTS

KEY POINTS

- ♦ **EPIRBS provides homing signals for search and rescue units.**
- ♦ **Operates on 406 Mhz frequency. In some instances 121.5 MHz is still used for beacon homing.**
- ♦ **121.5 MHz (still used for SAR direction finding) is replaced with 406 MHz. COSPAS satellites launched before 2006 and SARSAT satellites launched before 2009 will include the 121.5 MHz frequency.**
- ♦ **406 MHz gives better location accuracy, has global coverage and a unique identification beacon, which include distress information.**
- ♦ **EPIRBS must be registered with an appropriate authority. This ensures that details held on EPIRB registers are as accurate as possible.**

Testing

Each month, perform an internal test of the battery and transmitter:

- Wipe the EPIRB clean.
- Push the switch to the *TEST* position. The strobe and red light will flash after 15 seconds. After 1 minute the EPIRB will automatically reset.
- Check the expiry date of the battery.
- Enter the results in the GMDSS logbook.

Every 3 months:

- Visually check the holding bracket.

Every 2 years:

- Authorised agent should service EPIRB and renew the hydrostatic release.

Every 4 years - or as required by the manufacturer:

- Battery changed during service.

Search and Rescue Transponders

Purpose
The Search and Rescue Transponder (SART) assists the location of a vessel in distress or a survival craft.

The SART only responds when interrogated by a 9GHz (X-Band, 3 cm) radar. An activated SART displays, a dotted line on the interrogating radar.

Testing
Every month, activate the SART and check that a response is detected on the 9GHz/X-Band/3 cm radar.

- Release the SART from its holder.
- Ensure the vessel is in open water with no ships in the vicinity.
- Activate the self-test button. A red light will show the SART has been activated.
- When the radar beam interrogates the SART, an audible alarm will be heard.

- On the 3cm radar display, 12-20 dots will be seen coming from the SART location. These dots will develop into a pattern of concentric circles.
- Check the expiry date of the battery.
- Renew the battery at least every four years.
- Enter the results in the GMDSS logbook.

Hand Held VHF Radios

- Passenger and cargo ships over 500 tons must carry at least three portable VHF sets for use in survival craft.
- Cargo ships of under 500 tons should carry at least two portable VHF sets for use in survival craft.
- Each set should be waterproof.
- Each set shall be capable of receiving frequency 156.8 MHz (VHF Ch 16) on at least one channel.
- Keep the spare batteries for the sets fully charged at all times.

Immersion Suits and Thermal Protective Aids

Immersion Suits

- Operates in sea water temperature range -1°C to +30°C.

- The immersion suit permits the wearer to carry out normal duties.

- Immersion suit designed to withstand a jump from 4.5 metres with no ingress of water.

- The immersion suit will not allow the ingress of water up to a period of at least 20 minutes.

- If the suit has no inherent insulation, it should ensure that the core temperature of the body does not fall more than 2° in water of temperature 5° after 1 hour.

- If the suit has insulation, it should ensure that the core temperature of the body does not fall more than 2° in water of temperature between 0° and 2° after 6 hours.

- Fitted with retro-reflective tape to ease detection.

- Immersion suit is marked with: manufacturer's name, date of manufacture, size, serial number and instructions that warm clothing should be worn if the suit is not insulated.

Thermal Protective Aids

- Designed to cover the whole body of a person except the face whilst wearing a lifejacket.

- Functions properly in the temperature range of -30°C to +20°C and its purpose is to reduce the loss of heat from the wearer.

- It should be capable of being donned in a survival craft.

- If it impairs swimming it can be removed in not more than two minutes in the water.

Reference:
MGN 71 Musters, drills and decision making

Launching of Survival Craft

Launching Crews for Lifeboats and Rescue Boats

- Where the boat or launching device is not strong enough to allow the survival craft to be lowered with its full complement, paint a red band 150mm wide around the davit or launching device.

- When this band is displayed the boat, should be able to be launched by two persons.

- Attach a notice to the davit or launching device that states 'Lower or recover with 2 person crew only.'

- An annual service is required for liferafts, lifejackets, inflatable boats, rescue boats, fast rescue boats and hydrostatic release units.

Launching of Liferafts

- Attach the painter of the liferafts attached to a strong point on the ship.

- Hydrostatic release units (HRU) will activate at a depth of 2-4 metres and release the rafts to float to the surface.

- Once the (HRU) has activated the raft, it is still attached to the ship by the weak link. Once the raft is inflated, it will produce enough drag to let the raft to float free.

- To release the rafts manually, release the senhouse slip holding the lashings.

- With the painter is still attached to a strong point, throw the raft overboard, pull on the painter until the CO_2 bottle activates and inflates the raft.

Launching of Survival Craft

- Survival craft should be capable of being launched when the ship is listed up to 20° either way.

- 2 crewmembers should be able to prepare the boat for launching in no more than 5 minutes.

Reference:
MGN 78   Launching of crews for lifeboats, rescue boats, class C boats inflatable and other boats.
MGN 362 Servicing of inflatable liferafts, inflatable boats, rescue boats, fast rescue boats, inflatable lifejackets and hydrostatic release units.

Launching the Lifeboat	Recovering the Lifeboat
1. All personnel mustered.	1. Ensure brake lever on the boat deck is fully closed.
2. Rig the painter to a strong point forward of the davit.	
	2. Before coming alongside the falls reset the lifting hook mechanism.
3. Release the senhouse slip holding the gripes.	3. Connect the shipboard fall hooks to the lifeboat. Ensure the fall wire is not twisted.
4. Helmsman enters the lifeboat first, fits plug and prepares engine.	
5. All personnel enter lifeboat wearing lifejackets. Weight is evenly distributed around lifeboat.	4. Reset the hydrostatic release mechanism. Pull out the position-locking pin. Move the handle forward to the LOCKED position. Release the position-locking pin and insert safety pin.
6. Start the engine and leave it running in neutral.	
7. Lifeboat can be lowered with everyone inside by pulling on the brake wire. Alternatively the boat can be lowered manually by lifting the brake lever on the boat deck.	5. Visually check forward and aft falls cam release and lever arm in correct position.
	6. Commence hoisting the lifeboat.
	7. When the lifeboat is just clear of the water check the hydrostatic release indicator has moved to the OK position. Check that lever arms and cam release are still in correct positions.
8. When the lifeboat reaches the water. Release the brake wire. Release the falls hook quick release lever.	
9. To release falls. Ensure hydrostatic indicator is pointing to 'OK' position. Release the safety pin and pull the release handle back fully. The falls will now release.	8. Everyone in the boat seated. Continue hoisting.
	9. Turn off engine.
10. Check the falls are clear and have been released.	10. Limit switches will stop lifeboat just short of fully raised position.
11. Release the toggle painter and move clear of the vessel using the engine.	11. Disembark personnel.

The fall preventer device (FPD) should be engaged/disengaged in line with the manufacturers instructions, SMS and ships SOLAS training manual.

Reference:
MGN 445   Lifeboats: Fitting of 'Fall Preventer Devices' to Reduce the Danger of Accidental On-load Hook Release

Markings on Survival Craft

- Manufacturer's name and address. Month and year of manufacture.
- Lifeboat model and serial number.
- Number of persons the craft is approved to carry.

Markings on LSA Equipment

Equipment	Marking
Lifeboat	• Manufacturer's name and address. Month and year of manufacture. • Lifeboat model and serial number. • Number of persons the craft is approved to carry. • Name and port of registry on each side of the boat's bows. • Means of identifying the boat number and ship from the air. • Retro-reflective tape so the boat is visible to a searchlight looking horizontally and vertically.
Liferafts	• Fit retro-reflective tape round canopy. • Fit retro-reflective tape (in a cross) on the underside of the floor.
Lifebuoys	• Fit retro-reflective tape at four evenly-spaced points around the lifebuoy.
Buoyant Apparatus	• Fit retro-reflective tape in the same way as liferafts. Should be visible from the air as well as from sea.
Lifejackets	• Fit with retro-reflective tape as high up as possible to let it be seen from any direction.
Immersion Suits	• Fit with sufficient retro-reflective tape to aid search and rescue from the sea and air.

Reference:
MGN 105   Use and fitting of retro-reflective material on life saving appliances

Pyrotechnics

Type	Colour	Intensity Candela	Duration	Remarks
Rocket Flare	Red	30,000	40 seconds	Reaches height of 300 metres.
Hand Flare	Red	15,000	1 minute	Burns after being submerged for 10 secs in 100 mm of water.
Buoyant Smoke Signals	Orange		3 minutes	Burns after being submerged for 10 secs in 100 mm of water.
Line Throwing Appliances			Can throw 4 mm line 230 m in calm weather.	4 Projectiles. Maintain serviceability for 4 years.

Disposal of Out-of-Date Pyrotechnics

- Return them to the supplier directly - or through their agent.
- When liferafts are sent ashore for servicing, request the liferaft station to dispose of the pyrotechnics.
- Contact the local coastguard.

Reference:
MGN 419 Disposal of Out of Date Pyrotechnics (Marine Flares)

Launching and Recovery of Rescue Boat

- Rescue boat can be boarded and launched in not more than 5 minutes.
- Capable of being launched with the vessel making headway of up to 5 knots.
- It should be possible to recover a rescue boat with its full complement of crew and equipment.
- If the rescue boat is also a lifeboat, it should possible to recover it when loaded with lifeboat equipment and the rescue boat crew of 6 persons.

Launching the Rescue Boat	Recovering the Rescue Boat
1. Remove covers, lashings, and electric charging socket.	1. Ensure quick-release hook mechanism is reset in the rescue boat. Safety pin in place.
2. Rig the painter forward of the rescue boat.	2. Once alongside the ship, retrieve the painter and connect it to the painter release hook.
3. Rescue boat crew board the boat wearing appropriate clothing.	3. Attach the lifting hook to the falls.
4. Start the engine. When crew give OK, lower the boat.	4. All crew and passengers positioned correctly: begin hoisting the boat.
5. When approaching the water, the coxswain sets the boat controls for the conditions: (if the ship is moving ahead, the engine will be set appropriately).	5. Fully recover the boat and stop the engine.
6. With the boat in the water, the designated crew member removes the safety pin from the hook and stands clear.	6. Disembark all passengers and crew.
7. The coxswain then pulls the hook release handle until the hook is clear of the falls.	7. Secure the rescue boat for immediate relaunch.
8. Release the painter and use engines to move away from the vessel.	
9. Reset the quick-release mechanism and reset the safety pin.	

Reference:
SI 1999 Lifesaving 2721

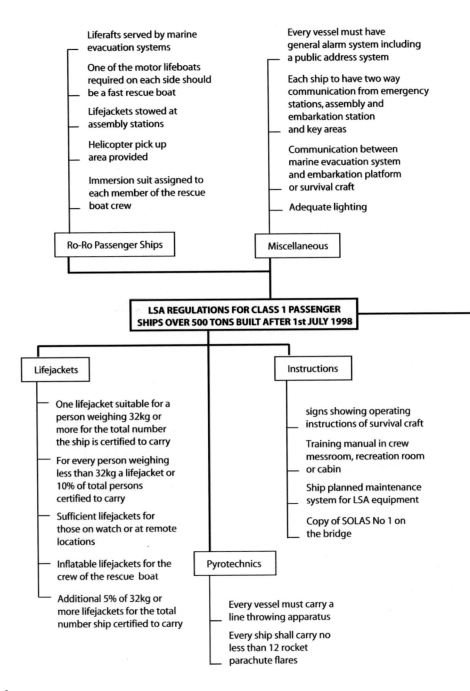

Ro-Ro Passenger Ships

- Liferafts served by marine evacuation systems
- One of the motor lifeboats required on each side should be a fast rescue boat
- Lifejackets stowed at assembly stations
- Helicopter pick up area provided
- Immersion suit assigned to each member of the rescue boat crew

Miscellaneous

- Every vessel must have general alarm system including a public address system
- Each ship to have two way communication from emergency stations, assembly and embarkation station and key areas
- Communication between marine evacuation system and embarkation platform or survival craft
- Adequate lighting

LSA REGULATIONS FOR CLASS 1 PASSENGER SHIPS OVER 500 TONS BUILT AFTER 1st JULY 1998

Lifejackets

- One lifejacket suitable for a person weighing 32kg or more for the total number the ship is certified to carry
- For every person weighing less than 32kg a lifejacket or 10% of total persons certified to carry
- Sufficient lifejackets for those on watch or at remote locations
- Inflatable lifejackets for the crew of the rescue boat
- Additional 5% of 32kg or more lifejackets for the total number ship certified to carry

Instructions

- signs showing operating instructions of survival craft
- Training manual in crew messroom, recreation room or cabin
- Ship planned maintenance system for LSA equipment
- Copy of SOLAS No 1 on the bridge

Pyrotechnics

- Every vessel must carry a line throwing apparatus
- Every ship shall carry no less than 12 rocket parachute flares

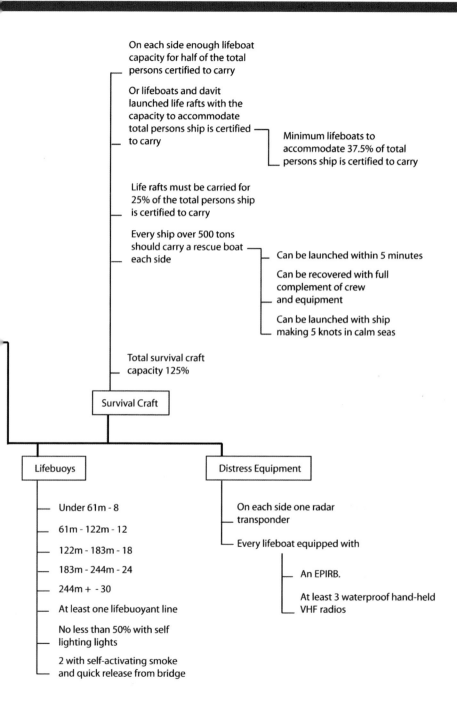

On each side enough lifeboat capacity for half of the total persons certified to carry

Or lifeboats and davit launched life rafts with the capacity to accommodate total persons ship is certified to carry

Minimum lifeboats to accommodate 37.5% of total persons ship is certified to carry

Life rafts must be carried for 25% of the total persons ship is certified to carry

Every ship over 500 tons should carry a rescue boat each side

Can be launched within 5 minutes

Can be recovered with full complement of crew and equipment

Can be launched with ship making 5 knots in calm seas

Total survival craft capacity 125%

Survival Craft

Lifebuoys

Under 61m - 8

61m - 122m - 12

122m - 183m - 18

183m - 244m - 24

244m + - 30

At least one lifebuoyant line

No less than 50% with self lighting lights

2 with self-activating smoke and quick release from bridge

Distress Equipment

On each side one radar transponder

Every lifeboat equipped with

An EPIRB.

At least 3 waterproof hand-held VHF radios

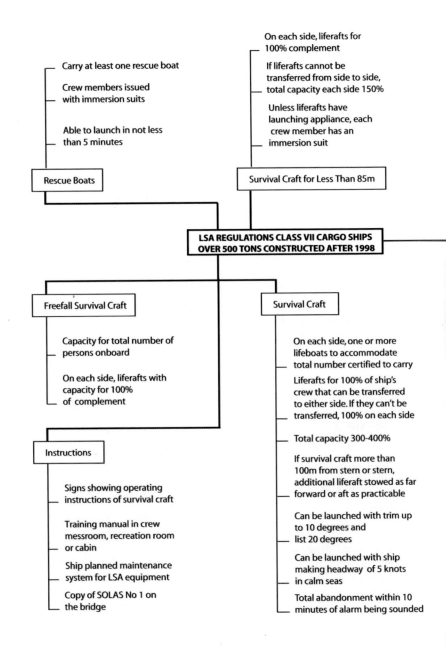

Rescue Boats

- Carry at least one rescue boat
- Crew members issued with immersion suits
- Able to launch in not less than 5 minutes

Survival Craft for Less Than 85m

- On each side, liferafts for 100% complement
- If liferafts cannot be transferred from side to side, total capacity each side 150%
- Unless liferafts have launching appliance, each crew member has an immersion suit

LSA REGULATIONS CLASS VII CARGO SHIPS OVER 500 TONS CONSTRUCTED AFTER 1998

Freefall Survival Craft

- Capacity for total number of persons onboard
- On each side, liferafts with capacity for 100% of complement

Instructions

- Signs showing operating instructions of survival craft
- Training manual in crew messroom, recreation room or cabin
- Ship planned maintenance system for LSA equipment
- Copy of SOLAS No 1 on the bridge

Survival Craft

- On each side, one or more lifeboats to accommodate total number certified to carry
- Liferafts for 100% of ship's crew that can be transferred to either side. If they can't be transferred, 100% on each side
- Total capacity 300-400%
- If survival craft more than 100m from stern or stern, additional liferaft stowed as far forward or aft as practicable
- Can be launched with trim up to 10 degrees and list 20 degrees
- Can be launched with ship making headway of 5 knots in calm seas
- Total abandonment within 10 minutes of alarm being sounded

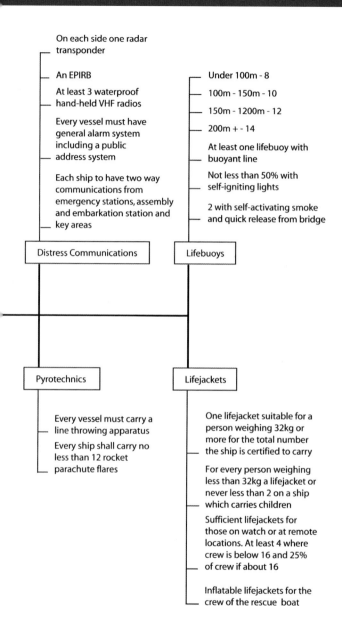

On each side one radar transponder

An EPIRB

At least 3 waterproof hand-held VHF radios

Every vessel must have general alarm system including a public address system

Each ship to have two way communications from emergency stations, assembly and embarkation station and key areas

Distress Communications

Under 100m - 8

100m - 150m - 10

150m - 1200m - 12

200m + - 14

At least one lifebuoy with buoyant line

Not less than 50% with self-igniting lights

2 with self-activating smoke and quick release from bridge

Lifebuoys

Pyrotechnics

Every vessel must carry a line throwing apparatus

Every ship shall carry no less than 12 rocket parachute flares

Lifejackets

One lifejacket suitable for a person weighing 32kg or more for the total number the ship is certified to carry

For every person weighing less than 32kg a lifejacket or never less than 2 on a ship which carries children

Sufficient lifejackets for those on watch or at remote locations. At least 4 where crew is below 16 and 25% of crew if about 16

Inflatable lifejackets for the crew of the rescue boat

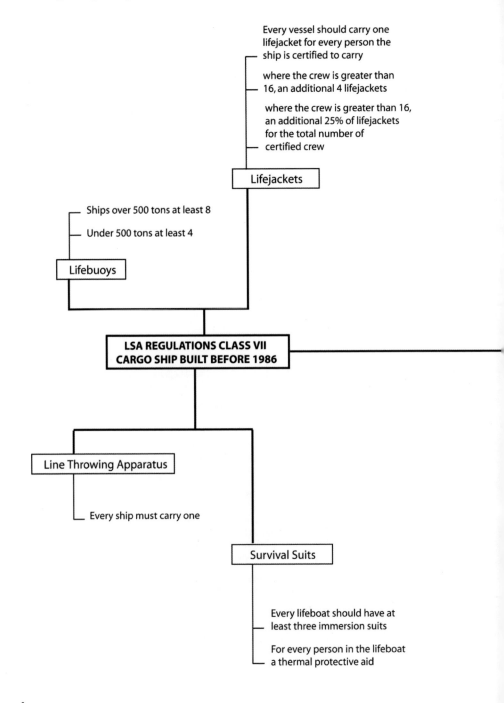

Every vessel should carry one lifejacket for every person the ship is certified to carry

where the crew is greater than 16, an additional 4 lifejackets

where the crew is greater than 16, an additional 25% of lifejackets for the total number of certified crew

Lifejackets

Ships over 500 tons at least 8

Under 500 tons at least 4

Lifebuoys

LSA REGULATIONS CLASS VII CARGO SHIP BUILT BEFORE 1986

Line Throwing Apparatus

Every ship must carry one

Survival Suits

Every lifeboat should have at least three immersion suits

For every person in the lifeboat a thermal protective aid

Each vessel shall carry an EPIRB

At least 3 waterproof VHF radios

At least 1 radar transponder on each side

Distress Communications

Survival Craft

Ships over 500t: on each side of the ship one or more lifeboats with the capacity for the total number onboard

Ships over 500t should also carry life rafts for the number the ship is certified to carry. At least two of these should be the same capacity

Ships 500 tons - 1600 tons may carry liferafts instead of lifeboats for the total number the ship is certified to carry. In addition, a Class C boat or inflatable boat should be carried

In vessels over 100m, additional liferafts should be deployed as far forward or aft as possible

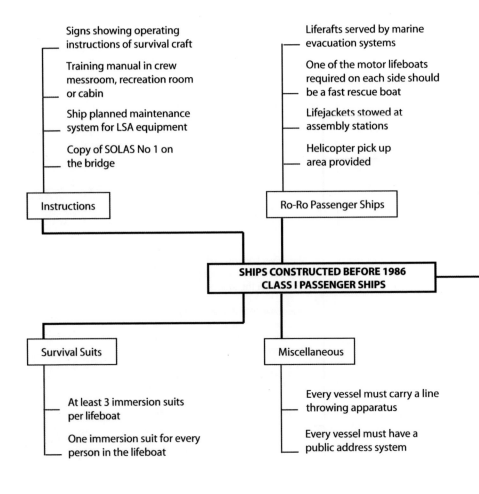

Signs showing operating
instructions of survival craft

Training manual in crew
messroom, recreation room
or cabin

Ship planned maintenance
system for LSA equipment

Copy of SOLAS No 1 on
the bridge

Instructions

Liferafts served by marine
evacuation systems

One of the motor lifeboats
required on each side should
be a fast rescue boat

Lifejackets stowed at
assembly stations

Helicopter pick up
area provided

Ro-Ro Passenger Ships

**SHIPS CONSTRUCTED BEFORE 1986
CLASS I PASSENGER SHIPS**

Survival Suits

At least 3 immersion suits
per lifeboat

One immersion suit for every
person in the lifeboat

Miscellaneous

Every vessel must carry a line
throwing apparatus

Every vessel must have a
public address system

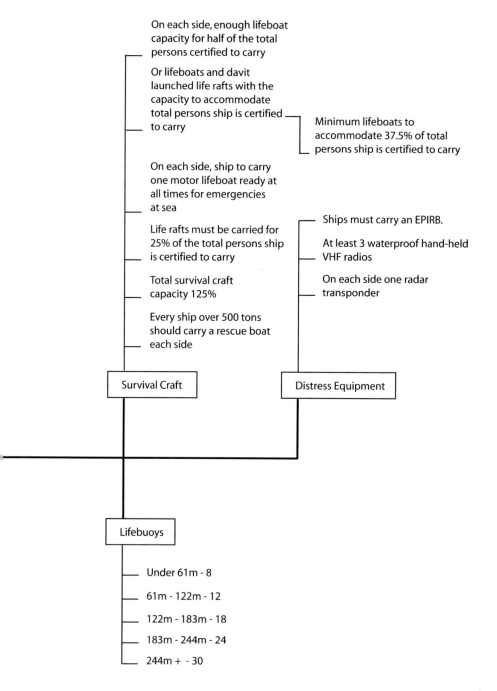

On each side, enough lifeboat capacity for half of the total persons certified to carry

Or lifeboats and davit launched life rafts with the capacity to accommodate total persons ship is certified to carry

Minimum lifeboats to accommodate 37.5% of total persons ship is certified to carry

On each side, ship to carry one motor lifeboat ready at all times for emergencies at sea

Life rafts must be carried for 25% of the total persons ship is certified to carry

Total survival craft capacity 125%

Every ship over 500 tons should carry a rescue boat each side

Ships must carry an EPIRB.

At least 3 waterproof hand-held VHF radios

On each side one radar transponder

Survival Craft

Distress Equipment

Lifebuoys

Under 61m - 8

61m - 122m - 12

122m - 183m - 18

183m - 244m - 24

244m + - 30

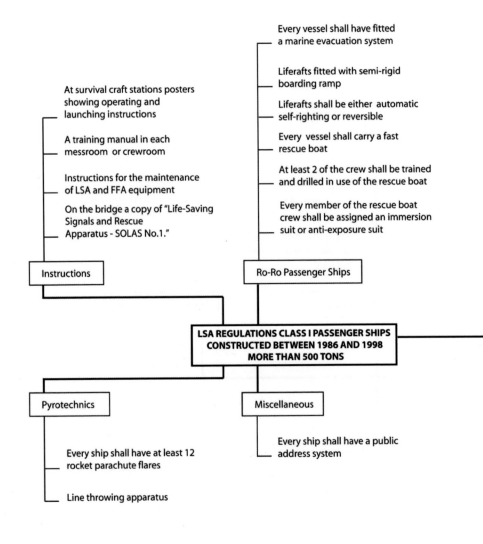

Every vessel shall have fitted a marine evacuation system

Liferafts fitted with semi-rigid boarding ramp

Liferafts shall be either automatic self-righting or reversible

Every vessel shall carry a fast rescue boat

At least 2 of the crew shall be trained and drilled in use of the rescue boat

Every member of the rescue boat crew shall be assigned an immersion suit or anti-exposure suit

At survival craft stations posters showing operating and launching instructions

A training manual in each messroom or crewroom

Instructions for the maintenance of LSA and FFA equipment

On the bridge a copy of "Life-Saving Signals and Rescue Apparatus - SOLAS No.1."

Instructions

Ro-Ro Passenger Ships

LSA REGULATIONS CLASS I PASSENGER SHIPS CONSTRUCTED BETWEEN 1986 AND 1998 MORE THAN 500 TONS

Pyrotechnics

Miscellaneous

Every ship shall have at least 12 rocket parachute flares

Line throwing apparatus

Every ship shall have a public address system

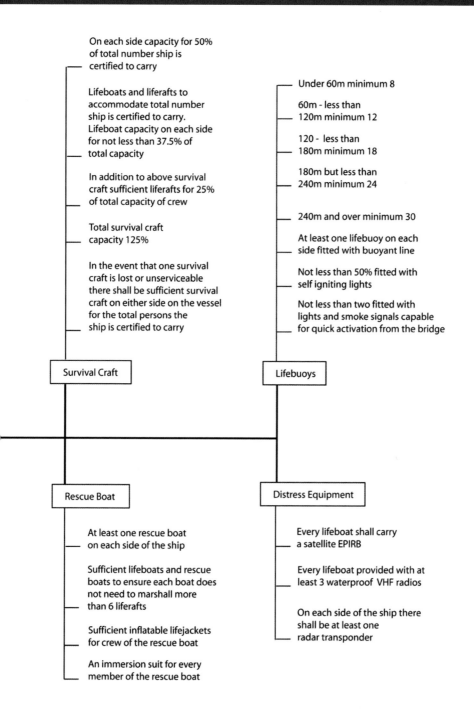

On each side capacity for 50% of total number ship is certified to carry

Lifeboats and liferafts to accommodate total number ship is certified to carry. Lifeboat capacity on each side for not less than 37.5% of total capacity

In addition to above survival craft sufficient liferafts for 25% of total capacity of crew

Total survival craft capacity 125%

In the event that one survival craft is lost or unserviceable there shall be sufficient survival craft on either side on the vessel for the total persons the ship is certified to carry

Survival Craft

Under 60m minimum 8

60m - less than 120m minimum 12

120 - less than 180m minimum 18

180m but less than 240m minimum 24

240m and over minimum 30

At least one lifebuoy on each side fitted with buoyant line

Not less than 50% fitted with self igniting lights

Not less than two fitted with lights and smoke signals capable for quick activation from the bridge

Lifebuoys

Rescue Boat

At least one rescue boat on each side of the ship

Sufficient lifeboats and rescue boats to ensure each boat does not need to marshall more than 6 liferafts

Sufficient inflatable lifejackets for crew of the rescue boat

An immersion suit for every member of the rescue boat

Distress Equipment

Every lifeboat shall carry a satellite EPIRB

Every lifeboat provided with at least 3 waterproof VHF radios

On each side of the ship there shall be at least one radar transponder

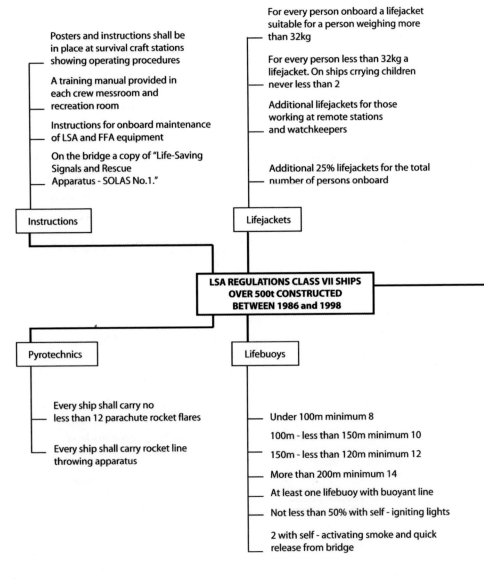

For every person onboard a lifejacket suitable for a person weighing more than 32kg

For every person less than 32kg a lifejacket. On ships crrying children never less than 2

Additional lifejackets for those working at remote stations and watchkeepers

Additional 25% lifejackets for the total number of persons onboard

Posters and instructions shall be in place at survival craft stations showing operating procedures

A training manual provided in each crew messroom and recreation room

Instructions for onboard maintenance of LSA and FFA equipment

On the bridge a copy of "Life-Saving Signals and Rescue Apparatus - SOLAS No.1."

Instructions

Lifejackets

LSA REGULATIONS CLASS VII SHIPS OVER 500t CONSTRUCTED BETWEEN 1986 and 1998

Pyrotechnics

Lifebuoys

Every ship shall carry no less than 12 parachute rocket flares

Every ship shall carry rocket line throwing apparatus

Under 100m minimum 8

100m - less than 150m minimum 10

150m - less than 120m minimum 12

More than 200m minimum 14

At least one lifebuoy with buoyant line

Not less than 50% with self - igniting lights

2 with self - activating smoke and quick release from bridge

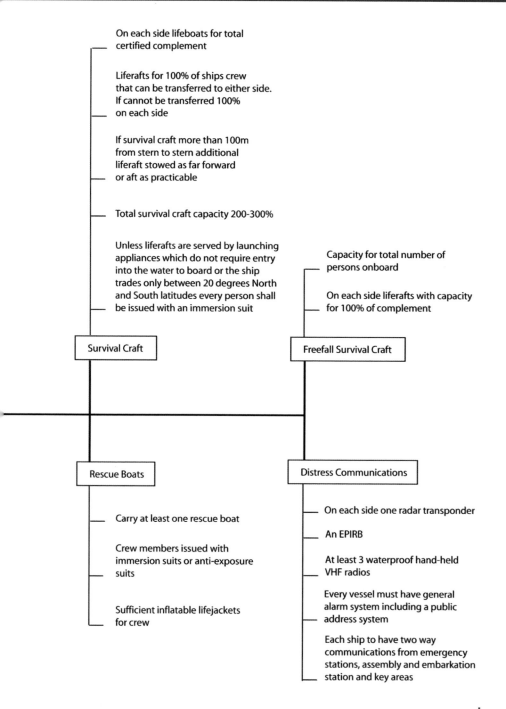

On each side lifeboats for total
certified complement

Liferafts for 100% of ships crew
that can be transferred to either side.
If cannot be transferred 100%
on each side

If survival craft more than 100m
from stern to stern additional
liferaft stowed as far forward
or aft as practicable

Total survival craft capacity 200-300%

Unless liferafts are served by launching
appliances which do not require entry
into the water to board or the ship
trades only between 20 degrees North
and South latitudes every person shall
be issued with an immersion suit

Capacity for total number of
persons onboard

On each side liferafts with capacity
for 100% of complement

Survival Craft

Freefall Survival Craft

Rescue Boats

Distress Communications

Carry at least one rescue boat

Crew members issued with
immersion suits or anti-exposure
suits

Sufficient inflatable lifejackets
for crew

On each side one radar transponder

An EPIRB

At least 3 waterproof hand-held
VHF radios

Every vessel must have general
alarm system including a public
address system

Each ship to have two way
communications from emergency
stations, assembly and embarkation
station and key areas

Sources of Medical Information

Radio Medical Advice for Ships at Sea

- Each European member state must designate a centre, which will provide medical advice to ships.
- The advice is free and will supplement advice in the Ship's Captain's Medical Guide.
- Initial contact is with HM Coastguard on MF DSC, VHF DSC, VHF Channel 16 or INMARSAT.

International Radio Medical Centre

- International Radio Medical centre (CIRM) based in Rome, Italy.
- Gives 24 hour, free radio medical assistance worldwide to ships of any country.
- Can co-ordinate the evacuation of a patient.

Ship Details to Pass On

- Vessels name and call sign.
- Position of vessel, port of departure, ETA, route and speed.
- What medicine chest is available

Patient Details

- Name age and nationality of patient.
- Temperature, blood pressure, pulse, respiratory rate.
- Symptoms, location and type of pain.
- Other medical problems.
- If the patient's condition is the result of an accident, how the accident took place.
- Any treatment already administered.

Reference:
Admiralty List of Radio Signals Volume 1

Shipboard
Operations

International Safety Management Code

Functional Requirements

- Safety and environmental policy must be in place.
- Levels of authority defined.
- Instructions and procedures to ensure the safe operation of the vessel laid down.
- Procedures in place for reporting accidents and non-conformities.

Responsibilities

Company To ensure adequate resources and shore based staff to allow the Designated Person Ashore (DPA) to perform his/her duties.

DPA The link between the company and the ship. The DPA has direct access to the highest level of management. Responsible for monitoring the safety and pollution prevention aspects of the ships operations.

Master Responsible for the implementation of the safety and environmental policy. Motivates the crew to observe the policy. Reviews safety management system (SMS) and reports any deficiencies.

Ship Operations

- Each ship must be properly manned. The seafarers qualified, certificated and medically fit.
- Procedures must be in place for ship familiarisation in both job and policies.
- Procedure in place for identifying training deficiencies.
- Ship procedures are clearly written down.
- Checklists for key tasks such as safety of ship and pollution prevention.

- Reporting system in place for hazards and non-conformities.
- Planned maintenance system in place.
- Effective procedure to control all documents and data related to the SMS.
- Company verification is achieved through internal audits.

ISM Code

Part A – Implementation

- Safety Management System
  Structured and documented system enabling personnel to implement policies.
- Document of Compliance
  Issued to the company.
- Safety Management Certificate
  Issued to the ship.

Part B – Certification and Verification

Document of Compliance

- Issued by the flag state and is evidence that the company complies with the ISM Code.
- It is valid only for the ship types that it lists.
- If it is withdrawn the Safety Management Certificate will also be withdrawn.
- Audited annually by flag state.
- A copy is held onboard the vessel.

Safety Management Certificate

- Issued to the ship and valid for 5 years.
- At least one intermediate audit between years 2 and 3.
- Can be withdrawn if there is a major non-conformity.

Interim Document of Compliance

- Valid for 12 months and issued to a newly established company.

Interim Safety Management Certificate

- Issued when a company takes on a new ship.
- Issued when a ship changes flag.
- Valid not more than 6 months.

KEY POINTS

♦ Adopted as legislation under chapter XI of SOLAS, *Special Measures to Enhance Maritime Security.*

♦ Ship must carry an International Ship Security Certificate. Valid 5 years.

♦ Objective is to clearly define roles and responsibilities of port facilities, ships, shipping companies and governments in order to enhance security on ships and at port facilities.

♦ Levels of security introduced. Each ship must carry a ship security plan, which details exactly what action the vessel will take whilst operating at each security level.

♦ Every ship must undergo a ship security assessment, which identifies any potential weaknesses in the vessels' structure and procedures regarding security. Steps must be introduced to eliminate these weaknesses.

Key Roles and Responsibilities

Ship Security Officer (SSO)

- Must have completed an approved SSO course.
- Undertakes regular security inspections of the vessel.
- Responsible for implementing the ship security plan and proposing any modifications.
- Reports to the Company Security Officer (CSO).
- Responsible for ensuring that all crew with specific security duties are trained in their tasks.
- Responsible for increasing the crews' security awareness. Each crew member should know exactly what security level the ship is operating on and what tasks that involves.
- Responsible for record keeping and reporting any reporting any breaches of security or non-conformities with the security plan to the CSO.

Master

- Ultimately responsible for the security of the vessel.
- Should liase closely with the SSO.
- Must have a detailed awareness of the ship security assessment and ship security plan.

Company Security Officer (CSO)

- Will advise the SSO on the level of threat at the next port.
- Ensures any deficiencies or non-conformities regarding the ship security plan are dealt with.
- Provides support to the SSO to enable him/her to carry out their duties.

Port Facilities Security Officer (PFSO)

- Ensures port facility security plan is implemented.
- Responsible for enhancing security awareness within the port.
- Liases with CSO and SSO regarding the level of threat in the port.

Levels of Threat

Security Level 1	Normal operating level for ships and ports.
Security Level 2	Enhanced security level.
Security Level 3	There is a specific threat to the ship or port facility.

- A ship may operate on a higher level of security than the port.
- A ship may never operate at a lower level of security that on which the port is operating.

Declaration of Security

- Contract between the port and the ship detailing the specific security duties and expectations of each party for the duration of the port call.

Training and Drills

- A security drill must be carried out at least every 3 months.
- If following a crew change more than 25% of the crew have not participated in a security drill on the ship in the last 3 months a drill must be conducted within 1 week.
- The ship should participate in a security exercise once every 12 months with no more than 18 months between exercises.

Risk Assessment

Definitions

- Hazard – A source of potential harms or damage. A situation with potential for harm or damage.

- Risk – The likelihood of a hazard occurring and what the consequences of this would be.

- Risk assessment – An examination of what may cause harm in order to permit sufficient precautions to be taken to prevent harm.

Application

- Assessment should be carried out for all work activities onboard the ship. Assessment should cover activities where there is a foreseeable element of risk attached.

- The company is responsible to ensure that risk assessment has taken place. A responsible person with suitable experience should carry out the assessment.

- Where there is no existing risk assessment in place for a task then an assessment should be carried out prior to the work commencing. All risk assessments should be reviewed periodically to take account of any change of procedure or equipment.

- When conducting a risk assessment there are 4 processes to go through.

1) Classify Work Activities	Work activities should be grouped in a logical order and information gathered about them. E.g. for working over the ships side. What department is responsible for the work? Where exactly will the work be carried out? Is the work planned maintenance? Exactly what activity will take place?
2) Identify the Hazards	Is there a source of harm? Who could be harmed? How could the harm happen?
3) Determine the Risk	How severe would the result of any harm be? How likely is it will happen?
4) Decide if the risk is tolerable.	Risks are estimated on the consequences of the harm occurring and the likelihood of it happening.

Duties of the Safety Committee

- Ensure the *Code of Safe Working Practice* is complied with.

- Seek to improve the standard and safety awareness among the crew.

- The committee may make representations to the employer on issues regarding potential hazards and dangerous occurrences onboard the vessel.

- The committee can request the safety officer to carry out investigations on workplace health and safety matters.

- The committee can inspect the safety officers' records.

- Records should be kept of all safety committee meetings.

Duties of the Safety Officer

- Ensure *Code of Safe Working Practice* and company health and safety policies complied with.

- Seek to improve the safety awareness among the crew.

- Investigate accidents, dangerous occurrences and potential hazards.

- Investigate health and safety crew complaints.

- Conduct health and safety inspections at least once every 3 months.

- Advise on statutory deficiencies, which may occur.

- Keep a record book of accidents and dangerous occurrences.

- Stop any work, which may be dangerous.

Duties of the Safety Representative

- Can participate in investigations conducted by the safety officer.

- Consults on health and safety matters with the Master and safety officer.

Reference:
SI 1997 2962

Shipboard Oil Pollution Emergency Plan

KEY POINTS

♦ Oil tankers over 150 gt and other vessels over 400 gt must carry a shipboard oil pollution emergency plan.

♦ Plans should be simple consisting of a series of checklists and flowcharts.

♦ The plan should guide the Master through the decisions and action required in responding to an incident.

♦ The plan should assist the crew in taking steps to minimize any discharge of oil.

♦ If the vessel also complies with the requirements of Annex II of MARPOL (Noxious Liquid Substance) the two plans may be combined in one document the 'Shipboard Marine Pollution Emergency Plan.'

Mandatory Contents of SOPEP

- The procedure to be followed by the Master in the event of an oil pollution incident.

- A list of authorities and persons to contact in the event of an oil pollution incident.

- Detailed procedure of action to be taken by the ships crew in order to reduce and stop the flow of oil from an incident.

- The procedures and contact details of the command centre on the bridge for co-ordinating national and local pollution control centres.

Non-Mandatory Contents of SOPEP

- Plans and diagrams of the ship.

- Oil spill response equipment carried on the vessel.

- Procedure for dealing with the media.

- Procedure for record keeping and collecting evidence.

- Procedure for reviewing and amending the plan.

- Details of drills.

Reference:
Annex I MARPOL 73/78 Regulation 26
MGN 231   Shipboard Pollution Emergency Plans: Guidance on their Development and Approval

Standards of Training Certification and Watchkeeping for Seafarers (STCW 95)

Five main areas where STCW 95 affects the ship.

Shipboard Familiarisation

- Seafarers must be familiarised with their specific duties and the shipboard arrangements. The ship familiarisation tour is carried out as soon as practical after a seafarer has joined the vessel. Among the areas covered are; location of muster stations and emergency equipment; procedures for routine and emergency drills; name of the safety officials onboard; procedure for accident reporting.

- The company must provide the Master with a set of polices and procedures to be followed. The seafarer should be made aware of these policies as part of the familiarisation tour.

Hours of Work

- Watchkeepers must have a minimum of 10 hours rest in a 24 hour period and 77 hours in any 7 day period.

- A record must be kept of all hours worked and this is available for inspection by port state.

- Companies are responsible for posting up watch schedules which give details for every position the daily work and rest periods at sea and in port.

- In the event of an emergency affecting the safety of the ship these hours may be exceeded.

- Further reference see MSN 1767 (M)

Training

- Under STCW 95 training for bridge watchkeepers in the use of ARPA, ECDIS, AIS and in bridge simulators is mandatory.

Medicals

- Medical standards were implemented under STCW95 and modified in 2011.

- Every seafarer must hold an ENG1 medical certificate. These certificates are valid for 2 years.

- The MCA publishes a list of approved practitioners who can issue the ENG1.

Certification

STCW 95 also stated the classes and restriction on certificates issued by an authority.

Title of Deck Certificates	Categories of Certificate
1) Master	II/2 500 gt or more
	II/2 3000 gt or more
	II/3 less than 500 gt (near coastal)
2) Chief Mate	II/2 500 gt or more
	II/2 3000 gt or more
	II/2 between 500 gt and 3000 gt
3) Officer of the Watch	II/1 500 gt or more
	II/3 less than 500 gt (near coastal)
4) Navigational Watch Rating	II/4 500 gt or more
5) Able Seafarer Deck	II/5 500 gt or more

Title of Engineering Certificates	Categories of Certificate
1) Chief Engineer	III/2 3000 kW or more
	III/3 between 750 and 3000 kW
2) Second Engineer	III/2 3000 kW or more
	III/3 between 750 kW and 3000 kW
3) Officer of The Watch	III/1 750kW or more
	III/3 less than 500 gt (near coastal)
4) Engineer Watch Rating	III/4 over 750 kW
5) Able Seafarer Engine	III/5

Title of Electro-technical Certificates	Categories of Certificate
1) Electro Technical Officer (ETO)	III/6 750 kW or more
2) Electro-technical Rating	III/7 750 kW or more

Annex I   Regulations for the Prevention of
Pollution by Oil

Shipboard Requirements

- Ships must carry International Oil Pollution Prevention certificate.

- Ships must carry oil record book.
  Part I Machinery Space Operations – records details of all ballasting, tank cleaning. Any discharging of ballast/cleaning water.
  Part II Cargo/Ballast Operations. Any loading, discharging, ballasting of cargo tanks and dedicated clean ballast tanks.

- Bilge pumping.
  For vessels other than tankers.
  Proceeding on voyage
  Ship outside a special area.
  Oil content not to exceed 15ppm.
  Oil discharge filtering and monitoring system fitted.

  For Tankers
  Tanker proceeding on voyage.
  Tanker outside special area.
  More than 50 miles from nearest land.
  Oil content less than 30 litres per mile.
  Total quantity discharged is less than 1/30000 of previous cargo.

Special Areas

No pumping or discharge from tankers under any circumstances.

- Mediterranean Sea
- Baltic Sea
- Black Sea
- Red Sea
- Gulf Area
- Antarctic Area
- Wider Caribbean
- North Sea

Annex II   Regulations for the Control of Pollution by Noxious Liquid Substances

- MSN 1703. The discharge of NLS into the sea is prohibited except where stated in MSN 1703.

- Noxious Liquid Substances divided into four categories A, B, C, D. Category A posing the greatest threat.

- Vessels must carry an emergency plan in the event of any incident.

Annex III   Regulations for the Prevention of Pollution by Harmful Substances Carried by Sea in Packaged Form.

- Harmful substances are identified in the IMDG Code.

- Carriage conditions for harmful substances can be found in the IMDG Code.

- All packages should be properly labelled, marked and accompanied by the correct documentation.

Sewage Special Area
(from 1 January 2013)

- Baltic Sea

Annex IV   Regulations for the Prevention of Pollution by Sewage from Ships.

- Ships must carry an International Sewage Pollution Prevention Certificate.

- Vessels must have sewage treatment plants onboard.

Annex V   Regulations for the Prevention of Pollution by Garbage from Ships.

- Ships must have a garbage management plan.

- Any treatment of garbage should be recorded in the garbage record book. This book is available for inspection by port state.

Garbage Special Areas

- Mediterranean Sea
- Baltic Sea
- Black Sea
- Red Sea
- Antarctic
- North Sea
- Wider Caribbean Area

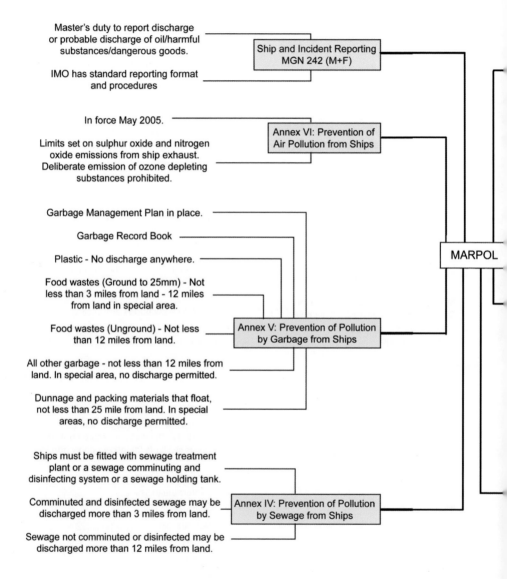

Master's duty to report discharge or probable discharge of oil/harmful substances/dangerous goods.

IMO has standard reporting format and procedures

Ship and Incident Reporting MGN 242 (M+F)

In force May 2005.

Limits set on sulphur oxide and nitrogen oxide emissions from ship exhaust. Deliberate emission of ozone depleting substances prohibited.

Annex VI: Prevention of Air Pollution from Ships

Garbage Management Plan in place.

Garbage Record Book

Plastic - No discharge anywhere.

Food wastes (Ground to 25mm) - Not less than 3 miles from land - 12 miles from land in special area.

Food wastes (Unground) - Not less than 12 miles from land.

All other garbage - not less than 12 miles from land. In special area, no discharge permitted.

Dunnage and packing materials that float, not less than 25 mile from land. In special areas, no discharge permitted.

Annex V: Prevention of Pollution by Garbage from Ships

Ships must be fitted with sewage treatment plant or a sewage comminuting and disinfecting system or a sewage holding tank.

Comminuted and disinfected sewage may be discharged more than 3 miles from land.

Sewage not comminuted or disinfected may be discharged more than 12 miles from land.

Annex IV: Prevention of Pollution by Sewage from Ships

MARPOL

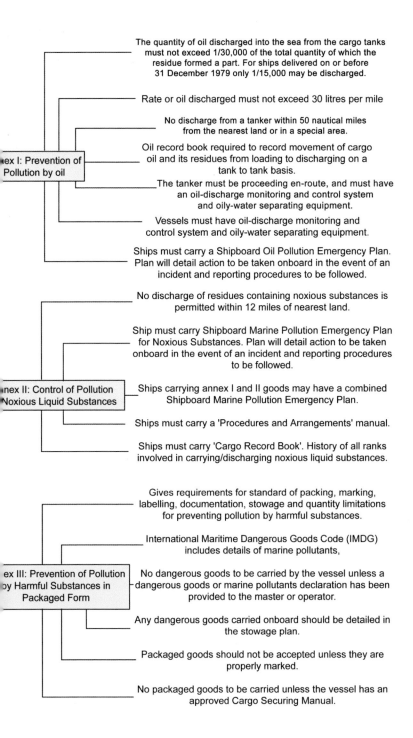

Annex I: Prevention of Pollution by oil

The quantity of oil discharged into the sea from the cargo tanks must not exceed 1/30,000 of the total quantity of which the residue formed a part. For ships delivered on or before 31 December 1979 only 1/15,000 may be discharged.

Rate or oil discharged must not exceed 30 litres per mile

No discharge from a tanker within 50 nautical miles from the nearest land or in a special area.

Oil record book required to record movement of cargo oil and its residues from loading to discharging on a tank to tank basis.

The tanker must be proceeding en-route, and must have an oil-discharge monitoring and control system and oily-water separating equipment.

Vessels must have oil-discharge monitoring and control system and oily-water separating equipment.

Ships must carry a Shipboard Oil Pollution Emergency Plan. Plan will detail action to be taken onboard in the event of an incident and reporting procedures to be followed.

Annex II: Control of Pollution Noxious Liquid Substances

No discharge of residues containing noxious substances is permitted within 12 miles of nearest land.

Ship must carry Shipboard Marine Pollution Emergency Plan for Noxious Substances. Plan will detail action to be taken onboard in the event of an incident and reporting procedures to be followed.

Ships carrying annex I and II goods may have a combined Shipboard Marine Pollution Emergency Plan.

Ships must carry a 'Procedures and Arrangements' manual.

Ships must carry 'Cargo Record Book'. History of all ranks involved in carrying/discharging noxious liquid substances.

Annex III: Prevention of Pollution by Harmful Substances in Packaged Form

Gives requirements for standard of packing, marking, labelling, documentation, stowage and quantity limitations for preventing pollution by harmful substances.

International Maritime Dangerous Goods Code (IMDG) includes details of marine pollutants,

No dangerous goods to be carried by the vessel unless a dangerous goods or marine pollutants declaration has been provided to the master or operator.

Any dangerous goods carried onboard should be detailed in the stowage plan.

Packaged goods should not be accepted unless they are properly marked.

No packaged goods to be carried unless the vessel has an approved Cargo Securing Manual.

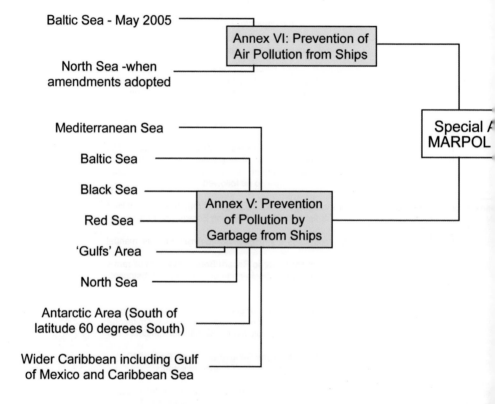

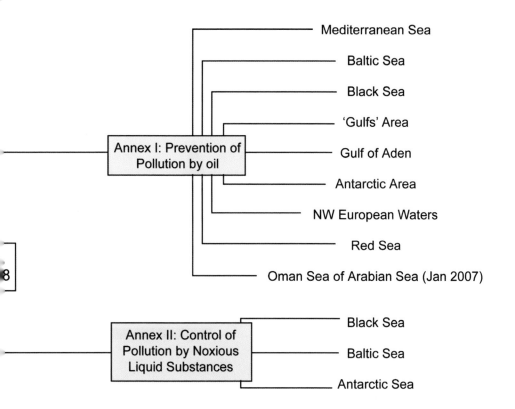

IALA Systems of Buoyage

IALA System A

Lateral Marks

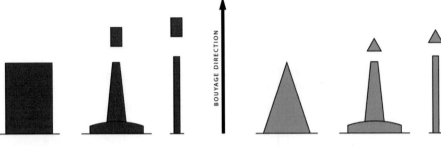

Colour: Red
Shape: Can, Pillar, Spar
Topmark (if fitted): Can

Colour: Green
Shape: Conical, pillar, spar
Topmark (if fitted) : green cone

Light: Any light rhythm except composite group flashing (2+1)

Preferred Channel Marks

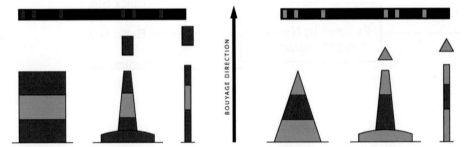

Found at a point where the channel divides. A vessel following the main channel would treat these buoys in the same way as a lateral mark.

Colour: Red with broad green band.
Shape: Can, Pillar, Spar
Topmark (if fitted): Can

Colour: Green with broad red band.
Shape: Conical, pillar, spar
Topmark (if fitted): green cone

Light: Composite group flashing (2+1)

IALA System B

Lateral Marks

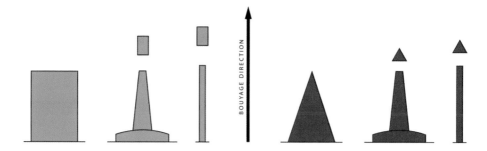

Colour: Green
Shape: Can, Pillar, Spar
Topmark (if fitted): Can

Colour: Red
Shape: Conical, pillar, spar
Topmark (if fitted): red cone

Light: Any light rhythm except composite group flashing (2+1)

Preferred Channel Marks

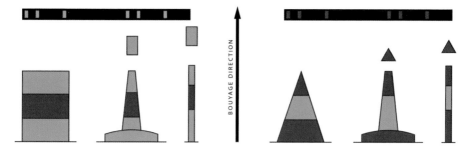

Found at a point where the channel divides. A vessel following the main channel would treat these buoys in the same way as a lateral mark.

Colour: Green with broad red band.
Shape: Can, Pillar, Spar
Topmark (if fitted): Green can

Colour: Red with broad green band Shape:
Conical, pillar, spar.
Topmark (if fitted): Red cone

Light: Composite group flashing (2+1)

Cardinal Marks

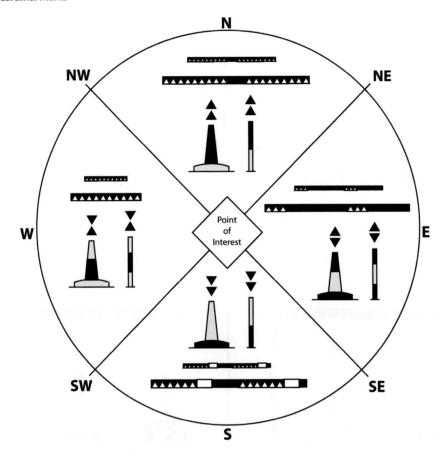

Name	Topmark	Colour	Reflector	Light
North Cardinal	Two cones points up	Black band above yellow band	Blue on black part yellow on yellow part	White light very quick or quick flashing
East Cardinal	Two cones points outward	Black bands above and below yellow bands	2 blue bands on upper black part	3 flashes VQ 5s Q 10s
South Cardinal	Two cones points down	Black band below yellow band	Yellow on yellow part blue on black part	6 + long flash VQ 10s Q 15s
West Cardinal	Two cones points inward	Black band with yellow bands above and below	2 yellow on upper yellow part	9 flashes VQ 10s Q 15s

Safe Water Mark

Indicates navigable water all around the buoy. Used as centreline, mid-channel or fairway buoy.

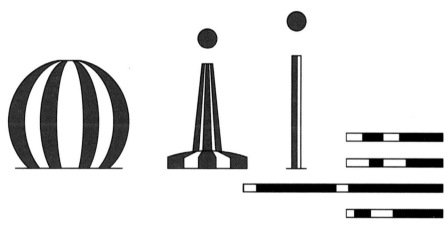

Colour: Red and white
Shape: Spherical, pillar or spar.
Topmark: Red sphere
Light: Isophase, Occulting, Long flash every 10s or morse A

Isolated Danger

Marks a danger of limited navigable extent with safe water all around it.

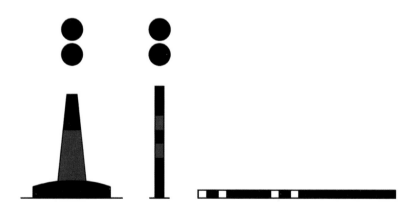

Colour: Black and red
Shape: Pillar or spar
Topmark: Two black spheres
Light: White group flash 2

Special Mark

Marks: Cables or pipelines, Recreation zones, Ocean
data acquisition system buoys (ODAS), Military
exercise zones, Traffic separation schemes, Spoil
grounds

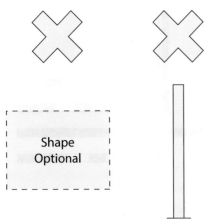

Colour: Yellow
Shape: Optional
Topmark: Yellow X
Light: Yellow, any rhythm not used for white
           lights

New Danger

New danger – newly discovered danger not yet
shown on charts or promulgated by Notices to
Mariners or included in Sailing Directions. Can be
naturally occurring e.g. rocks or man made e.g.
wrecks.

One or more cardinal marks

- New danger or lateral marks.
- If the danger is grave on or more of the marks
  may be duplicated until the danger has been
  promulgated.
- New danger cardinal mark will show white
  light quick or very quick.
- New danger lateral mark will show red or
  green light quick or very quick.
- Racon Morse code D with signal length 1 mile
  may be used to mark a new danger

Emergency Wreck-Marking Buoy

Approved by the IMO in 2007 Emergency
Wreck-Marking Buoys are temporarily used until
the wreck is well known/publicised in nautical
publications, has been fully surveyed and exact
details are established and a permanent form of
marking is in place.

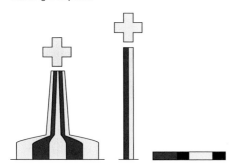

Colour:	Blue and yellow vertical stripes
Shape:	Pillar or spar
Topmark:	Standing/upright yellow cross
Light:	Alternating blue and yellow 1s flashes with 0.5s interval
Racon:	Morse D and/or AIS transponder

Buoyage Regions

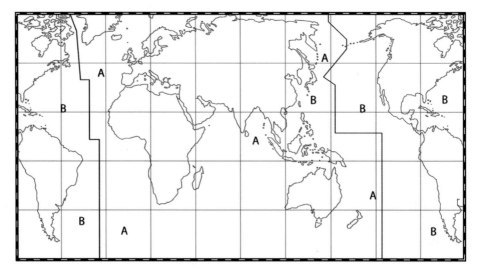

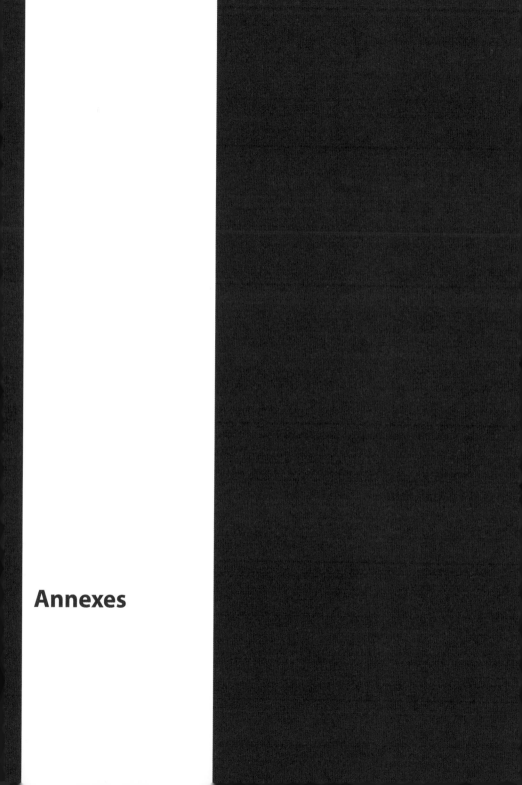

Annexes

The Merchant Shipping (Distress Signals and Prevention of Collisions) Regulations 1996

Notice to Owners, Masters, Skippers, Officers and Crews of Merchant Ships, Fishing Vessels, Pleasure Vessels, Yachts and Other Seagoing Craft.

This notice takes immediate effect and supersedes MSN M.1642/COLREG 1

Summary

This Notice and the Rules referred to in it are an integral part of the Merchant Shipping (Distress Signals and Prevention of Collisions) Regulations 1996, which came into force on 1 May 1996. These Regulations implement the Convention on the International Regulations for Preventing Collisions at Sea, 1972, as amended. They enhance safe navigation, by prescribing the conduct of vessels underway, specify the display of internationally-understood lights and sound signals and set out collision avoidance actions in close quarter situations.

This notice incorporates amendments to the International Regulations for Preventing Collisions at Sea, 1972, up to and including those annexed to IMO Resolution A.910(22). In accordance with the Convention, the latest amendments come into force internationally on 29 November 2003.

Introduction

1. This Notice and the Rules referred to in it are an integral part of the Merchant Shipping (Distress Signals and Prevention of Collisions) Regulations 1996, which came into force on 1 May 1996. These Regulations implement the Convention on the International Regulations for Preventing Collisions at Sea, 1972, as amended.

Latest Amendments

2. This notice incorporates amendments to the International Regulations for Preventing Collisions at Sea, 1972, up to and including those annexed to IMO Resolution A.910(22).

3. The amendments include:
Extension of the *General definitions* of *vessel* to include Wing-In-Ground Craft (WIG) with amendment to rules 3, 18, 23 and 31;

Revision of *Action to avoid collision* Rule 8;
Revision of *Equipment for sound signals* Rule 33

Revision to *Sound signals in restricted visibility* Rule 35; and

Annexes I, *Positioning and Technical Details of Lights and Shapes* and III, *Technical Details of Sound Signals.*

Note on the Application of the Regulations

4. The application of these Rules is limited through the Regulations, to the vessels or ships as defined in the Merchant Shipping Act 1995. Application to craft falling outside of this definition e.g. WIGs, personal water craft and others; will therefore be subject to a Maritime and Coastguard Agency (MCA) opinion of what it considers to be good conduct and practice by the

owners, operators and those in charge of such craft.

5. Extension of the Regulations to cover a broader range of vessel types by use of powers granted to the Secretary of State under the Railways and Transport Safety Act 2003, section 112; is currently under consideration.

Important reminder

6. From a recommendation as a result of an investigation into a collision that occurred in the Dover Strait in 2002, mariners are reminded that sections II and III of the Steering and Sailing Rules must be strictly complied with. However, vessels are not prevented from taking sufficiently early action ahead of the point in time at which those sections of the Rules come into effect.

Background

7. In these Regulations -

(1) The traffic separation schemes referred to in Rule 10(a) are the schemes listed in Notice to Mariners No 17 of the Annual Summary and marked "*" in the margin;

(2) The diagram mentioned in paragraph 7 of Annex I is the diagram specified in the Chromaticity Chart (1975) published by the International Illumination Commission (CIE); and

(3) The International Code of Signals referred to in paragraph 3 of Annex IV is published by the International Maritime Organization.

Navigation & Communication
Maritime and Coastguard Agency
Spring Place
105 Commercial Road
Southampton
SO15 1EG

Telephone: 023 8032 9523
Fax: 023 8032 9204
E-Mail: Navcomms@mcga.gov.uk

MCA Website Address:
http://www.mcga.gov.uk

File Ref: MNA 127/013/0002

Published: 05/2004

Safer Lives, Safer Ships, Cleaner Seas

Department for
Transport

The MCA is an executive agency
of the Department for Transport

Table of Contents of the International Regulations

INTERNATIONAL REGULATIONS FOR PREVENTING COLLISIONS AT SEA, 1972

(as amended by Resolutions A464(XII), A626(15), A678(16), A736(18) and A.910(22))

PART A - GENERAL

Rule 1

Application

(a) These Rules shall apply to all vessels upon the high seas and in all waters connected therewith navigable by seagoing vessels.

(b) Nothing in these Rules shall interfere with the operation of special rules made by an appropriate authority for roadsteads, harbours, rivers, lakes or inland waterways connected with the high seas and navigable by seagoing vessels. Such special rules shall conform as closely as possible to these Rules.

(c) Nothing in these Rules shall interfere with the operation of any special rules made by the Government of any State with respect to additional station or signal lights, shapes or whistle signals for ships of war and vessels proceeding under convoy, or with respect to additional station or signal lights or shapes for fishing vessels engaged in fishing as a fleet. These additional station or signal lights, shapes or whistle signals shall, so far as possible, be such that they cannot be mistaken for any light, shape or signal authorised elsewhere under these Rules.

(d) Traffic separation schemes may be adopted by the Organization for the purpose of these Rules.

(e) Whenever the Government concerned shall have determined that a vessel of any special construction or purpose cannot comply with the provisions of any of these Rules with respect to the number, position, range or arc of visibility of lights or shapes, as well as to the disposition and characteristics of sound-signalling appliances, such vessel shall comply with such other provisions in regard to the number, position, range or arc of visibility of lights or shapes, as well as to the disposition and characteristics of sound-signalling appliances, as her Government shall have determined to be the closest possible compliance with these Rules in respect of that vessel.

Rule 2

Responsibility

(a) Nothing in these Rules shall exonerate any vessel, or the owner, master or crew thereof, from the consequences of any neglect to comply with these Rules or of the neglect of any precaution which may be required by the ordinary practice of seamen, or by the special circumstances of the case.

(b) In construing and complying with these Rules due regard shall be had to all dangers of navigation and collision and to any special circumstances, including the limitations of the vessels involved, which may make a departure from these Rules necessary to avoid immediate danger.

Rule 3

General definitions

For the purpose of these Rules, except where the context otherwise requires:

(a)   The word "vessel" includes every description of water craft, including non-displacement craft, WIG craft and seaplanes, used or capable of being used as a means of transportation on water.

(b)   The term "power-driven vessel" means any vessel propelled by machinery.

(c)   The term "sailing vessel" means any vessel under sail provided that propelling machinery, if fitted, is not being used.

(d)   The term "vessel engaged in fishing" means any vessel fishing with nets, lines, trawls or other fishing apparatus which restrict manoeuvrability, but does not include a vessel fishing with trolling lines or other fishing apparatus which do not restrict manoeuvrability.

(e)   The word "seaplane" includes any aircraft designed to manoeuvre on the water.

(f)   The term "vessel not under command" means a vessel which through some exceptional circumstance is unable to manoeuvre as required by these Rules and is therefore unable to keep out of the way of another vessel.

(g)   The term "vessel restricted in her ability to manoeuvre" means a vessel which from the nature of her work is restricted in her ability to manoeuvre as required by these Rules and is therefore unable to keep out of the way of another vessel. The term "vessels restricted in their ability to manoeuvre" shall include but not be limited to:

    (i)   a vessel engaged in laying, servicing or picking up a navigation mark, submarine cable or pipeline;

    (ii)   a vessel engaged in dredging, surveying or underwater operations;

    (iii)   a vessel engaged in replenishment or transferring persons, provisions or cargo while underway;

    (iv)   a vessel engaged in the launching or recovery of aircraft;

    (v)   a vessel engaged in mine clearance operations;

    (vi)   a vessel engaged in a towing operation such as severely restricts the towing vessel and her tow in their ability to deviate from their course.

(h)   The term "vessel constrained by her draught" means a power-driven vessel which, because of her draught in relation to the available depth and width of navigable water, is severely restricted in her ability to deviate from the course she is following.

(i)   The word "underway" means that a vessel is not at anchor, or made fast to the shore, or aground.

(j)   The words "length" and "breadth" of a vessel mean her length overall and greatest breadth.

(k)   Vessels shall be deemed to be in sight of one another only when one can be observed visually from the other.

(l)   The term "restricted visibility" means any condition in which visibility is restricted by fog, mist, falling snow, heavy rainstorms, sandstorms or any other similar causes.

(m)   The term "Wing-in-Ground (WIG) craft" means a multimodal craft which, in its main operational mode, flies in close proximity to the surface by utilizing surface-effect action.

PART B - STEERING AND SAILING RULES

Section I - Conduct of vessels in any condition of visibility

Rule 4

Application

Rules in this Section apply in any condition of visibility.

Rule 5

Look-out

Every vessel shall at all times maintain a proper look-out by sight and hearing as well as by all available means appropriate in the prevailing circumstances and conditions so as to make a full appraisal of the situation and of the risk of collision.

Rule 6

Safe speed

Every vessel shall at all times proceed at a safe speed so that she can take proper and effective action to avoid collision and be stopped within a distance appropriate to the prevailing circumstances and conditions.

In determining a safe speed the following factors shall be among those taken into account:

(a)   By all vessels:

(i)   the state of visibility;

(ii)   the traffic density including concentrations of fishing vessels or any other vessels;

(iii)   the manoeuvrability of the vessel with special reference to stopping distance and turning ability in the prevailing conditions;

(iv)   at night the presence of background light such as from shore lights or from back scatter of her own lights;

(v)   the state of wind, sea and current, and the proximity of navigational hazards;

(vi)   the draught in relation to the available depth of water.

(b)   Additionally, by vessels with operational radar:

    (i)   the characteristics, efficiency and limitations of the radar equipment;

    (ii)   any constraints imposed by the radar range scale in use;

    (iii)   the effect on radar detection of the sea state, weather and other sources of interference;

    (iv)   the possibility that small vessels, ice and other floating objects may not be detected by radar at an adequate range;

    (v)   the number, location and movement of vessels detected by radar;

    (vi)   the more exact assessment of the visibility that may be possible when radar is used to determine the range of vessels or other objects in the vicinity.

Rule 7

Risk of collision

(a)   Every vessel shall use all available means appropriate to the prevailing circumstances and conditions to determine if risk of collision exists. If there is any doubt such risk shall be deemed to exist.

(b)   Proper use shall be made of radar equipment if fitted and operational, including long-range scanning to obtain early warning of risk of collision and radar plotting or equivalent systematic observation of detected objects.

(c)   Assumptions shall not be made on the basis of scanty information, especially scanty radar information.

(d)   In determining if risk of collision exists the following considerations shall be among those taken into account:

    (i)   such risk shall be deemed to exist if the compass bearing of an approaching vessel does not appreciably change;

    (ii)   such risk may sometimes exist even when an appreciable bearing change is evident, particularly when approaching a very large vessel or a tow or when approaching a vessel at close range.

Rule 8

Action to avoid collision

(a) Any action taken to avoid collision shall be taken in accordance with the Rules of this Part and shall, if the circumstances of the case admit, be positive, made in ample time and with due regard to the observance of good seamanship.

(b) Any alteration of course and/or speed to avoid collision shall, if the circumstances of the case admit, be large enough to be readily apparent to another vessel observing visually or by radar; a succession of small alterations of course and/or speed should be avoided.

(c) If there is sufficient sea-room, alteration of course alone may be the most effective action to avoid a close-quarters situation provided that it is made in good time, is substantial and does not result in another close-quarters situation.

(d) Action taken to avoid collision with another vessel shall be such as to result in passing at a safe distance. The effectiveness of the action shall be carefully checked until the other vessel is finally past and clear.

(e) If necessary to avoid collision or allow more time to assess the situation, a vessel shall slacken her speed or take all way off by stopping or reversing her means of propulsion.

(f) (i) A vessel which, by any of these Rules, is required not to impede the passage or safe passage of another vessel shall, when required by the circumstances of the case, take early action to allow sufficient sea-room for the safe passage of the other vessel.

    (ii) A vessel required not to impede the passage or safe passage of another vessel is not relieved of this obligation if approaching the other vessel so as to involve risk of collision and shall, when taking action, have full regard to the action which may be required by the Rules of this Part.

    (iii) A vessel the passage of which is not to be impeded remains fully obliged to comply with the Rules of this Part when the two vessels are approaching one another so as to involve risk of collision.

Rule 9

Narrow channels

(a) A vessel proceeding along the course of a narrow channel or fairway shall keep as near to the outer limit of the channel or fairway which lies on her starboard side as is safe and practicable.

(b) A vessel of less than 20 metres in length or a sailing vessel shall not impede the passage of a vessel which can safely navigate only within a narrow channel or fairway.

(c) A vessel engaged in fishing shall not impede the passage of any other vessel navigating within a narrow channel or fairway.

(d) A vessel shall not cross a narrow channel or fairway if such crossing impedes the passage of a vessel which can safely navigate only within such channel or fairway. The latter vessel may use the sound signal prescribed in Rule 34(d) if in doubt as to the intention of the crossing vessel.

(e) (i) In a narrow channel or fairway when overtaking can take place only if the vessel to be overtaken has to take action to permit safe passing, the vessel intending to overtake shall indicate her intention by sounding the appropriate signal prescribed in Rule 34(c)(i). The vessel to be overtaken shall, if in agreement, sound the appropriate signal prescribed in Rule 34(c)(ii) and take steps to permit safe passing. If in doubt she may sound the signals prescribed in Rule 34(d).

(ii) This Rule does not relieve the overtaking vessel of her obligation under Rule 13.

(f) A vessel nearing a bend or an area of a narrow channel or fairway where other vessels may be obscured by an intervening obstruction shall navigate with particular alertness and caution and shall sound the appropriate signal prescribed in Rule 34(e).

(g) Any vessel shall, if the circumstances of the case admit, avoid anchoring in a narrow channel.

Rule 10

Traffic separation schemes

(a) This Rule applies to traffic separation schemes adopted by the Organization and does not relieve any vessel of her obligation under any other Rule.

(b) A vessel using a traffic separation scheme shall:

(i) proceed in the appropriate traffic lane in the general direction of traffic flow for that lane;

(ii) so far as practicable keep clear of a traffic separation line or separation zone;

(iii) normally join or leave a traffic lane at the termination of the lane, but when joining or leaving from either side shall do so at as small an angle to the general direction of traffic flow as practicable.

(c) A vessel shall, so far as practicable, avoid crossing traffic lanes but if obliged to do so shall cross on a heading as nearly as practicable at right angles to the general direction of traffic flow.

(d) (i) A vessel shall not use an inshore traffic zone when she can safely use the appropriate traffic lane within the adjacent traffic separation scheme. However, vessels of less than 20 metres in length, sailing vessels and vessels engaged in fishing may use the inshore traffic zone.

(ii) Notwithstanding sub-paragraph (d) (i), a vessel may use an inshore traffic zone when en route to or from a port, offshore installation or structure, pilot station or any other place situated within the inshore traffic zone, or to avoid immediate danger.

(e) A vessel other than a crossing vessel or a vessel joining or leaving a lane shall not normally enter a separation zone or cross a separation line except:

(i) in cases of emergency to avoid immediate danger;

(ii) to engage in fishing within a separation zone.

(f) A vessel navigating in areas near the terminations of traffic separation schemes shall do so with particular caution.

(g)   A vessel shall so far as practicable avoid anchoring in a traffic separation scheme or in areas near its terminations.

(h)   A vessel not using a traffic separation scheme shall avoid it by as wide a margin as is practicable.

(i)   A vessel engaged in fishing shall not impede the passage of any vessel following a traffic lane.

(j)   A vessel of less than 20 metres in length or a sailing vessel shall not impede the safe passage of a power-driven vessel following a traffic lane.

(k)   A vessel restricted in her ability to manoeuvre when engaged in an operation for the maintenance of safety of navigation in a traffic separation scheme is exempted from complying with this Rule to the extent necessary to carry out the operation.

(l)   A vessel restricted in her ability to manoeuvre when engaged in an operation for the laying, servicing or picking up of a submarine cable, within a traffic separation scheme, is exempted from complying with this Rule to the extent necessary to carry out the operation.

Section II - Conduct of vessels in sight of one another

Rule 11

Application

Rules in this Section apply to vessels in sight of one another.

Rule 12

Sailing Vessels

(a)   When two sailing vessels are approaching one another, so as to involve risk of collision, one of them shall keep out of the way of the other as follows:

        (i)   when each has the wind on a different side, the vessel which has the wind on the port side shall keep out of the way of the other;

        (ii)   when both have the wind on the same side, the vessel which is to windward shall keep out of the way of the vessel which is to leeward;

        (iii)   if a vessel with the wind on the port side sees a vessel to windward and cannot determine with certainty whether the other vessel has the wind on the port or on the starboard side, she shall keep out of the way of the other.

(b)   For the purposes of this Rule the windward side shall be deemed to be the side opposite to that on which the mainsail is carried or, in the case of a square-rigged vessel, the side opposite to that on which the largest fore-and-aft sail is carried.

Rule 13

Overtaking

(a)   Notwithstanding anything contained in the Rules of Part B, Sections I and II, any vessel overtaking any other shall keep out of the way of the vessel being overtaken.

(b)   A vessel shall be deemed to be overtaking when coming up with another vessel from a direction more than 22.5 degrees abaft her beam, that is, in such a position with reference to the vessel she is overtaking, that at night she would be able to see only the stern light of that vessel but neither of her sidelights.

(c)   When a vessel is in any doubt as to whether she is overtaking another, she shall assume that this is the case and act accordingly.

(d)   Any subsequent alteration of the bearing between the two vessels shall not make the overtaking vessel a crossing vessel within the meaning of these Rules or relieve her of the duty of keeping clear of the overtaken vessel until she is finally past and clear.

Rule 14

Head-on situation

(a)   When two power-driven vessels are meeting on reciprocal or nearly reciprocal courses so as to involve risk of collision each shall alter her course to starboard so that each shall pass on the port side of the other.

(b)   Such a situation shall be deemed to exist when a vessel sees the other ahead or nearly ahead and by night she would see the mast head lights of the other in a line or nearly in a line and or both sidelights and by day she observes the corresponding aspect of the other vessel.

(c)   When a vessel is in any doubt as to whether such a situation exists she shall assume that it does exist and act accordingly.

Rule 15

Crossing situation

When two power-driven vessels are crossing so as to involve risk of collision, the vessel which has the other on her own starboard side shall keep out of the way and shall, if the circumstances of the case admit, avoid crossing ahead of the other vessel.

Rule 16

Action by give-way vessel

Every vessel which is directed to keep out of the way of another vessel shall, so far as possible, take early and substantial action to keep well clear.

Rule 17

Action by stand-on vessel

(a)   (i)   Where one of two vessels is to keep out of the way the other shall keep her course and speed.

        (ii)   The latter vessel may however take action to avoid collision by her manoeuvre alone, as soon as it becomes apparent to her that the vessel required to keep out of the way is not taking appropriate action in compliance with these Rules.

(b)   When, from any cause, the vessel required to keep her course and speed finds herself so close that collision cannot be avoided by the action of the give-way vessel alone, she shall take such action as will best aid to avoid collision.

(c)   A power-driven vessel which takes action in a crossing situation in accordance with sub-paragraph (a)(ii) of this Rule to avoid collision with another power-driven vessel shall, if the circumstances of the case admit, not alter course to port for a vessel on her own port side.

(d)   This Rule does not relieve the give-way vessel of her obligation to keep out of the way.

Rule 18

Responsibilities between vessels

Except where Rules 9,10 and 13 otherwise require:

(a)   A power-driven vessel underway shall keep out of the way of:

    (i)   a vessel not under command;

    (ii)   a vessel restricted in her ability to manoeuvre;

    (iii)   a vessel engaged in fishing;

    (iv)   a sailing vessel.

(b)   A sailing vessel underway shall keep out of the way of:

    (i)   a vessel not under command;

    (ii)   a vessel restricted in her ability to manoeuvre;

    (iii)   a vessel engaged in fishing.

(c)   A vessel engaged in fishing when underway shall, so far as possible, keep out of the way of:

    (i)   a vessel not under command;

    (ii)   a vessel restricted in her ability to manoeuvre.

(d)   (i)   Any vessel other than a vessel not under command or a vessel restricted in her ability to manoeuvre shall, if the circumstances of the case admit, avoid impeding the safe passage of a vessel constrained by her draught, exhibiting the signals in Rule 28.

    (ii)   A vessel constrained by her draught shall navigate with particular caution having full regard to her special condition.

(e)   A seaplane on the water shall, in general, keep well clear of all vessels and avoid impeding their navigation. In circumstances, however, where risk of collision exists, she shall comply with the Rules of this Part.

(f)   (i)   A WIG craft shall, when taking off, landing and in flight near the surface, keep well clear of all other vessels and avoid impeding their navigation;

    (ii)   A WIG craft operating on the water surface shall comply with the Rules of this Part as a power-driven vessel.

Section III - Conduct of vessels in restricted visibility

Rule 19

Conduct of vessels in restricted visibility

(a) This Rule applies to vessels not in sight of one another when navigating in or near an area of restricted visibility.

(b) Every vessel shall proceed at a safe speed adapted to the prevailing circumstances and conditions of restricted visibility. A power-driven vessel shall have her engines ready for immediate manoeuvre.

(c) Every vessel shall have due regard to the prevailing circumstances and conditions of restricted visibility when complying with the Rules of Section I of this Part.

(d) A vessel which detects by radar alone the presence of another vessel shall determine if a close-quarters situation is developing and/or risk of collision exists. If so, she shall take avoiding action in ample time, provided that when such action consists of an alteration of course, so far as possible the following shall be avoided:

    (i) an alteration of course to port for a vessel forward of the beam, other than for a vessel being overtaken;

    (ii) an alteration of course towards a vessel abeam or abaft the beam.

(e) Except where it has been determined that a risk of collision does not exist, every vessel which hears apparently forward of her beam the fog signal of another vessel, or which cannot avoid a close-quarters situation with another vessel forward of her beam, shall reduce her speed to the minimum at which she can be kept on her course. She shall if necessary take all her way off and in any event navigate with extreme caution until danger of collision is over.

PART C - LIGHTS AND SHAPES

Rule 20

Application

(a) Rules in this Part shall be complied with in all weathers.

(b) The Rules concerning lights shall be complied with from sunset to sunrise and during such times no other lights shall be exhibited, except such lights as cannot be mistaken for the lights specified in these Rules or do not impair their visibility or distinctive character, or interfere with the keeping of a proper look-out.

(c) The lights prescribed by these Rules shall, if carried, also be exhibited from sunrise to sunset in restricted visibility and may be exhibited in all other circumstances when it is deemed necessary.

(d) The Rules concerning shapes shall be complied with by day.

(e) The lights and shapes specified in these Rules shall comply with the provisions of Annex I to these Regulations.

Rule 21

Definitions

(a) "Masthead light" means a white light placed over the fore and aft centreline of the vessel showing an unbroken light over an arc of the horizon of 225 degrees and so fixed as to show the light from right ahead to 22.5 degrees abaft the beam on either side of the vessel.

(b) "Sidelights" means a green light on the starboard side and a red light on the port side each showing an unbroken light over an arc of the horizon of 112.5 degrees and so fixed as to show the light from the right ahead to 22.5 degrees abaft the beam on its respective side. In a vessel of less than 20 metres in length the sidelights may be combined in one lantern carried on the fore and aft centreline of the vessel.

(c) "Sternlight" means a white light placed as nearly as practicable at the stern showing an unbroken light over an arc of the horizon of 135 degrees and so fixed as to show the light 67.5 degrees from right aft on each side of the vessel.

(d) "Towing light" means a yellow light having the same characteristics as the "sternlight" defined in paragraph (c) of this Rule.

(e) "All-round light" means a light showing an unbroken light over an arc of the horizon of 360 degrees.

(f) "Flashing light" means a light flashing at regular intervals at a frequency of 120 flashes or more per minute.

Rule 22

Visibility of lights

The lights prescribed in these Rules shall have an intensity as specified in Section 8 of Annex I to these Regulations so as to be visible at the following minimum ranges:

(a) In vessels of 50 metres or more in length:

- a masthead light, 6 miles;

- a sidelight, 3 miles;

- a stern light, 3 miles;

- a towing light, 3 miles;

- a white, red, green or yellow all-round light, 3 miles.

(b) In vessels of 12 metres or more in length but less than 50 metres in length:

- a masthead light, 5 miles; except that where the length of the vessel is less than 20 metres, 3 miles;

- a sidelight, 2 miles;

- a sternlight, 2 miles;

- a towing light, 2 miles;

- a white, red, green or yellow all-round light, 2 miles.

(c)   In vessels of less than 12 metres in length:

- a masthead light, 2 miles;

- a sidelight, 1 mile;

- a sternlight, 2 miles;

- a towing light, 2 miles

- a white, red, green or yellow all-round light, 2 miles.

(d)   In inconspicuous, partly submerged vessels or objects being towed:

- a white all-round light, 3 miles.

Rule 23

Power-driven vessels underway

(a)   A power-driven vessel underway shall exhibit:

    (i)   a masthead light forward;

    (ii)   a second masthead light abaft of and higher than the forward one; except that a vessel of less than 50 metres in length shall not be obliged to exhibit such light but may do so;

    (iii)   sidelights;

    (iv)   a sternlight.

(b)   An air-cushion vessel when operating in the non-displacement mode shall, in addition to the lights prescribed in paragraph (a) of this Rule, exhibit an all-round flashing yellow light.

(c)   A WIG craft only when taking off, landing and in flight near the surface shall, in addition to the lights prescribed in paragraph (a) of this Rule, exhibit a high intensity all-round flashing red light.

(d)   (i)   A power-driven vessel of less than 12 metres in length may in lieu of the lights prescribed in paragraph (a) of this Rule exhibit an all-round white light and sidelights;

    (ii)   a power-driven vessel of less than 7 metres in length whose maximum speed does not exceed 7 knots may in lieu of the lights prescribed in paragraph (a) of this Rule exhibit an all-round white light and shall, if practicable, also exhibit sidelights;

    (iii)   the masthead light or all-round white light on a power-driven vessel of less than 12 metres in length may be displaced from the fore and aft centre line of the vessel if centreline fitting is not practicable, provided that the sidelights are combined in one lantern which shall be carried on the fore and aft centre line of the vessel or located as nearly as practicable in the same fore and aft line as the masthead light or the all-round white light.

Rule 24

Towing and pushing

(a) A power-driven vessel when towing shall exhibit:

 (i) instead of the light prescribed in Rule 23(a)(i) or (a)(ii), two masthead lights in a vertical line. When the length of the tow, measuring from the stern of the towing vessel to the after end of the tow exceeds 200 metres, three such lights in a vertical line;

 (ii) sidelights;

 (iii) a sternlight;

 (iv) a towing light in a vertical line above the sternlight;

 (v) when the length of the tow exceeds 200 metres, a diamond shape where it can best be seen.

(b) When a pushing vessel and a vessel being pushed ahead are rigidly connected in a composite unit they shall be regarded as a power-driven vessel and exhibit the lights prescribed in Rule 23.

(c) A power-driven vessel when pushing ahead or towing alongside, except in the case of a composite unit, shall exhibit:

 (i) instead of the light prescribed in Rule 23(a)(i) or (a)(ii), two masthead lights in a vertical line;

 (ii) sidelights;

 (iii) a sternlight.

(d) A power-driven vessel to which paragraph (a) or (c) of this Rule applies shall also comply with Rule 23(a) (ii).

(e) A vessel or object being towed, other than those mentioned in paragraph (g) of this Rule, shall exhibit:

 (i) sidelights;

 (ii) a sternlight;

 (iii) when the length of the tow exceeds 200 metres, a diamond shape where it can best be seen.

(f)   Provided that any number of vessels being towed alongside or pushed in a group shall be lighted as one vessel,

   (i)   a vessel being pushed ahead, not being part of a composite unit, shall exhibit at the forward end sidelights;

   (ii)   a vessel being towed alongside shall exhibit a sternlight and at the forward end, sidelights.

(g)   An inconspicuous, partly submerged vessel or object, or combination of such vessels or objects being towed, shall exhibit:

   (i)   if it is less than 25 metres in breadth, one all-round white light at or near the forward end and one at or near the after end except that dracones need not exhibit a light at or near the forward end;

   (ii)   if it is 25 metres or more in breadth, two additional all-round white lights at or near the extremities of its breadth;

   (iii)   if it exceeds 100 metres in length, additional all-round white lights between the lights prescribed in sub-paragraphs (i) and (ii) so that the distance between the lights shall not exceed 100 metres;

   (iv)   a diamond shape at or near the aftermost extremity of the last vessel or object being towed and if the length of the tow exceeds 200 metres an additional diamond shape where it can best be seen and located as far forward as is practicable.

(h)   Where from any sufficient cause it is impracticable for a vessel or object being towed to exhibit the lights or shapes prescribed in paragraph (e) or (g) of this Rule, all possible measures shall be taken to light the vessel or object towed or at least to indicate the presence of such vessel or object.

(i)   Where from any sufficient cause it is impracticable for a vessel not normally engaged in towing operations to display the lights prescribed in paragraph (a) or (c) of this Rule, such vessel shall not be required to exhibit those lights when engaged in towing another vessel in distress or otherwise in need of assistance. All possible measures shall be taken to indicate the nature of the relationship between the towing vessel and the vessel being towed as authorized by Rule 36, in particular by illuminating the towline.

Rule 25

Sailing vessels underway and vessels under oars

(a)   A sailing vessel underway shall exhibit:

   (i)   sidelights;

   (ii)   a sternlight.

(b)   In a sailing vessel of less than 20 metres in length the lights prescribed in paragraph (a) of this Rule may be combined in one lantern carried at or near the top of the mast where it can best be seen.

(c)   A sailing vessel underway may, in addition to the lights prescribed in paragraph (a) of this Rule, exhibit at or near the top of the mast, where they can best be seen, two all-round lights in a vertical line, the upper being red and the lower green, but these lights shall not be exhibited in conjunction with the combined lantern permitted by paragraph (b) of this Rule.

(d)   (i)   A sailing vessel of less than 7 metres in length shall, if practicable, exhibit the lights prescribed in paragraph (a) or (b) of this Rule, but if she does not, she shall have ready at hand an electric torch or lighted lantern showing a white light which shall be exhibited in sufficient time to prevent collision.

       (ii)   A vessel under oars may exhibit the lights prescribed in this Rule for sailing vessels, but if she does not, she shall have ready at hand an electric torch or lighted lantern showing a white light which shall be exhibited in sufficient time to prevent collision.

(e)   A vessel proceeding under sail when also being propelled by machinery shall exhibit forward where it can best be seen a conical shape, apex downwards.

Rule 26

Fishing Vessels

(a)   A vessel engaged in fishing, whether underway or at anchor, shall exhibit only the lights and shapes prescribed in this Rule.

(b)   A vessel when engaged in trawling, by which is meant the dragging through the water of a dredge net or other apparatus used as a fishing appliance, shall exhibit:

       (i)   two all-round lights in a vertical line, the upper being green and the lower white, or a shape consisting of two cones with their apexes together in a vertical line one above the other;

       (ii)   a masthead light abaft of and higher than the all-round green light; a vessel of less than 50 metres in length shall not be obliged to exhibit such a light but may do so;

       (iii) when making way through the water, in addition to the lights prescribed in this paragraph, sidelights and a stern light.

(c)   A vessel engaged in fishing, other than trawling, shall exhibit:

       (i)   two all-round lights in a vertical line, the upper being red and the lower white, or a shape consisting of two cones with apexes together in a vertical line one above the other;

       (ii)   when there is outlying gear extending more than 150 metres horizontally from the vessel, an all- round white light or a cone apex upwards in the direction of the gear;

       (iii) when making way through the water, in addition to the lights prescribed in this paragraph, sidelights and a sternlight.

(d)   The additional signals described in Annex II to these Regulations apply to a vessel engaged in fishing in close proximity to other vessels engaged in fishing.

(e)   A vessel when not engaged in fishing shall not exhibit the lights or shapes prescribed in this Rule, but only those prescribed for a vessel of her length.

Rule 27

*Vessels not under command or restricted in
their ability to manoeuvre*

(a)　A vessel not under command shall exhibit:

 (i) two all-round red lights in a vertical line where they can best be seen;

 (ii) two balls or similar shapes in a vertical line where they can best be seen;

 (iii) when making way through the water, in addition to the lights prescribed in this paragraph, sidelights and a stern light.

(b)　A vessel restricted in her ability to manoeuvre, except a vessel engaged in mine-clearance operations, shall exhibit:

 (i) three all-round lights in a vertical line where they can best be seen. The highest and lowest of these lights shall be red and the middle light shall be white;

 (ii) three shapes in a vertical line where they can best be seen. The highest and lowest of these shapes shall be balls and the middle one a diamond;

 (iii) when making way through the water, a masthead light or lights, sidelights and a sternlight, in addition to the lights prescribed in sub-paragraph (i);

 (iv) when at anchor, in addition to the lights or shapes prescribed in sub-paragraphs (i) and (ii), the light, lights or shape prescribed in Rule 30.

(c)　A power-driven vessel engaged in a towing operation such as severely restricts the towing vessel and her tow in their ability to deviate from their course shall, in addition to the lights or shapes prescribed in Rule 24(a), exhibit the lights or shapes prescribed in sub-paragraphs (b)(i) and (ii) of this Rule.

(d)　A vessel engaged in dredging or underwater operations, when restricted in her ability to manoeuvre, shall exhibit the lights and shapes prescribed in sub-paragraphs (b) (i), (ii) and (iii) of this Rule and shall in addition, when an obstruction exists, exhibit:

 (i) two all-round red lights or two balls in a vertical line to indicate the side on which the obstruction exists;

 (ii) two all-round green lights or two diamonds in a vertical line to indicate the side on which another vessel may pass;

 (iii) when at anchor, the lights or shapes prescribed in this paragraph instead of the lights or shape prescribed in Rule 30.

(e)　Whenever the size of a vessel engaged in diving operations makes it impracticable to exhibit all lights and shapes prescribed in paragraph (d) of this Rule, the following shall be exhibited:

 (i) three all-round lights in a vertical line where they can best be seen. The highest and lowest of these lights shall be red and the middle light shall be white;

 (ii) a rigid replica of the International Code flag "A" not less than 1 metre in height. Measures shall be taken to ensure its all-round visibility.

(f)   A vessel engaged in mine-clearance operations shall in addition to the lights prescribed for a power-driven vessel in Rule 23 or to the lights or shape prescribed for a vessel at anchor in Rule 30 as appropriate, exhibit three all-round green lights or three balls. One of these lights or shapes shall be exhibited near the foremast head and one at each end of the fore yard. These lights or shapes indicate that it is dangerous for another vessel to approach within 1000 metres of the mine clearance vessel.

(g)   Vessels of less than 12 metres in length, except those engaged in diving operations, shall not be required to exhibit the lights and shapes prescribed in this Rule.

(h)   The signals prescribed in this Rule are not signals of vessels in distress and requiring assistance. Such signals are contained in Annex IV to these Regulations.

Rule 28

Vessels constrained by their draught

A vessel constrained by her draught may, in addition to the lights prescribed for power-driven vessels in Rule 23, exhibit where they can best be seen three all-round red lights in a vertical line, or a cylinder.

Rule 29

Pilot vessels

(a)   A vessel engaged on pilotage duty shall exhibit:

   (i)   at or near the masthead, two all-round lights in a vertical line, the upper being white and the lower red;

   (ii)   when underway, in addition, sidelights and a sternlight;

   (iii)   when at anchor, in addition to the lights prescribed in sub-paragraph (i), the light, lights or shape prescribed in Rule 30 for vessels at anchor.

(b)   A pilot vessel when not engaged on pilotage duty shall exhibit the lights or shapes prescribed for a similar vessel of her length.

Rule 30

Anchored vessels and vessels aground

(a)   A vessel at anchor shall exhibit where it can best be seen:

   (i)   in the fore part, an all-round white light or one ball;

(ii)   at or near the stern and at a lower level than the light prescribed in sub-paragraph (i), an all-round white light.

(b)   A vessel of less than 50 metres in length may exhibit an all-round white light where it can best be seen instead of the lights prescribed in paragraph (a) of this Rule.

(c)   A vessel at anchor may, and a vessel of 100 metres and more in length shall, also use the available working or equivalent lights to illuminate her decks.

(d)   A vessel aground shall exhibit the lights prescribed in paragraph (a) or (b) of this Rule and in addition, where they can best be seen:

(i)   two all-round red lights in a vertical line;

(ii)   three balls in a vertical line.

(e)   A vessel of less than 7 metres in length, when at anchor, not in or near a narrow channel, fairway or anchorage, or where other vessels normally navigate, shall not be required to exhibit the lights or shape prescribed in paragraphs (a) and (b) of this Rule.

(f)   A vessel of less than 12 metres in length, when aground, shall not be required to exhibit the lights or shapes prescribed in sub-paragraphs (d) (i) and (ii) of this Rule.

Rule 31

Seaplanes

Where it is impracticable for a seaplane or a WIG craft to exhibit lights and shapes of the characteristics or in the positions prescribed in the Rules of this Part she shall exhibit lights and shapes as closely similar in characteristics and position as is possible.

PART D - SOUND AND LIGHT SIGNALS

Rule 32

Definitions

(a)   The word "whistle" means any sound signalling appliance capable of producing the prescribed blasts and which complies with the specifications in Annex III to these Regulations.

(b)   The term "short blast" means a blast of about one second's duration.

(c)   The term "prolonged blast" means a blast of from four to six seconds' duration.

Rule 33

Equipment for sound signals

(a)   A vessel of 12 metres or more in length shall be provided with a whistle, a vessel of 20 metres or more in length shall be provided with a bell in addition to a whistle, and a vessel of 100 metres or more in length shall, in addition, be provided with a gong, the tone and sound of which cannot be confused with that of the bell. The whistle, bell and gong shall comply with the specifications in Annex III to these Regulations. The bell or gong or both may be replaced by other equipment having the same respective sound characteristics, provided that manual sounding of the prescribed signals shall always be possible.

(b)   A vessel of less than 12 metres in length shall not be obliged to carry the sound signalling appliances prescribed in paragraph (a) of this Rule but if she does not, she shall be provided with some other means of making an efficient sound signal.

Rule 34

Manoeuvring and warning signals

(a)   When vessels are in sight of one another, a power-driven vessel underway, when manoeuvring as authorized or required by these Rules, shall indicate that manoeuvre by the following signals on her whistle:

- one short blast to mean "I am altering my course to starboard";

- two short blasts to mean "I am altering my course to port";

- three short blasts to mean "I am operating astern propulsion".

(b)   Any vessel may supplement the whistle signals prescribed in paragraph (a) of this Rule by light signals, repeated as appropriate, whilst the manoeuvre is being carried out:

    (i)   these light signals shall have the following significance

- one flash to mean "I am altering my course to starboard";

- two flashes to mean "I am altering my course to port";

- three flashes to mean "I am operating astern propulsion";

    (ii)   the duration of each flash shall be about one second, the interval between flashes shall be about one second, and the interval between successive signals shall be not less than ten seconds;

    (iii)   the light used for this signal shall, if fitted, be an all-round white light, visible at a minimum range of 5 miles, and shall comply with the provisions of Annex I to these Regulations.

(c)   When in sight of one another in a narrow channel or fairway:

    (i)   a vessel intending to overtake another shall in compliance with Rule 9(e)(i) indicate her intention by the following signals on her whistle:

- two prolonged blasts followed by one short blast to mean "I intend to overtake you on your starboard side";

- two prolonged blasts followed by two short blasts to mean "I intend to overtake you on your port side".

    (ii)   the vessel about to be overtaken when acting in accordance with Rule 9(e)(i) shall indicate her agreement by the following signal on her whistle:

- one prolonged, one short, one prolonged and one short blast, in that order.

(d)   When vessels in sight of one another are approaching each other and from any cause either vessel fails to understand the intentions or actions of the other, or is in doubt whether sufficient action is being taken by the other to avoid collision, the vessel in doubt shall immediately indicate such doubt by giving at least five short and rapid blasts on the whistle. Such signal may be supplemented by a light signal of at least five short and rapid flashes.

(e)   A vessel nearing a bend or an area of a channel or fairway where other vessels may be obscured by an intervening obstruction shall sound one prolonged blast. Such signal shall be answered with a prolonged blast by any approaching vessel that may be within hearing around the bend or behind the intervening obstruction.

(f)   If whistles are fitted on a vessel at a distance apart of more than 100 metres, one whistle only shall be used for giving manoeuvring and warning signals.

Rule 35

Sound signals in restricted visibility

In or near an area of restricted visibility, whether by day or night, the signals prescribed in this Rule shall be used as follows:

(a)   A power-driven vessel making way through the water shall sound at intervals of not more than 2 minutes one prolonged blast.

(b)   A power-driven vessel underway but stopped and making no way through the water shall sound at intervals of not more than 2 minutes two prolonged blasts in succession with an interval of about 2 seconds between them.

(c)   A vessel not under command, a vessel restricted in her ability to manoeuvre, a vessel constrained by her draught, a sailing vessel, a vessel engaged in fishing and a vessel engaged in towing or pushing another vessel shall, instead of the signals prescribed in paragraphs (a) or (b) of this Rule, sound at intervals of not more than 2 minutes three blasts in succession, namely one prolonged followed by two short blasts.

(d)   A vessel engaged in fishing, when at anchor, and a vessel restricted in her ability to manoeuvre when carrying out her work at anchor, shall instead of the signals prescribed in paragraph (g) of this Rule sound the signal prescribed in paragraph (c) of this Rule.

(e)   A vessel towed or if more than one vessel is towed the last vessel of the tow, if manned, shall at intervals of not more than 2 minutes sound four blasts in succession, namely one prolonged followed by three short blasts. When practicable, this signal shall be made immediately after the signal made by the towing vessel.

(f)   When a pushing vessel and a vessel being pushed ahead are rigidly connected in a composite unit they shall be regarded as a power-driven vessel and shall give the signals prescribed in paragraphs (a) or (b) of this Rule.

(g)   A vessel at anchor shall at intervals of not more than one minute ring the bell rapidly for about 5 seconds. In a vessel of 100 metres or more in length the bell shall be sounded in the forepart of the vessel and immediately after the ringing of the bell the gong shall be sounded rapidly for about 5 seconds in the after part of the vessel. A vessel at anchor may in addition sound three blasts in succession, namely one short, one prolonged and one short blast, to give warning of her position and of the possibility of collision to an approaching vessel.

(h)   A vessel aground shall give the bell signal and if required the gong signal prescribed in paragraph (g) of this Rule and shall, in addition, give three separate and distinct strokes on the bell immediately before and after the rapid ringing of the bell. A vessel aground may in addition sound an appropriate whistle signal.

(i)   A vessel of 12 metres or more but less than 20 metres in length shall not be obliged to give the bell signals prescribed in paragraphs (g) and (h) of this Rule. However, if she does not, she shall make some other efficient sound signal at intervals of not more than 2 minutes.

(j)   A vessel of less than 12 metres in length shall not be obliged to give the above-mentioned signals but, if she does not, shall make some other efficient sound signal at intervals of not more than 2 minutes.

(k)   A pilot vessel when engaged on pilotage duty may in addition to the signals prescribed in paragraphs (a),(b) or (g) of this Rule sound an identity signal consisting of four short blasts.

Rule 36

Signals to attract attention

If necessary to attract the attention of another vessel any vessel may make light or sound signals that cannot be mistaken for any signal authorised elsewhere in these Rules, or may direct the beam of her searchlight in the direction of the danger, in such a way as not to embarrass any vessel. Any light to attract the attention of another vessel shall be such that it cannot be mistaken for any aid to navigation. For the purpose of this Rule the use of high intensity intermittent or revolving lights, such as strobe lights, shall be avoided.

Rule 37

Distress signals

When a vessel is in distress and requires assistance she shall use or exhibit the signals described in Annex IV to these Regulations.

PART F - EXEMPTIONS

Rule 38

Exemptions

Any vessel (or class of vessels) provided that she complies with the requirements of the International Regulations for Preventing Collisions at Sea, *1960* (a), the keel of which is laid or which is at a corresponding stage of construction before the entry into force of these Regulations may be exempted from compliance therewith as follows:

(a)   The installation of lights with ranges prescribed in Rule 22, until 4 years after the date of entry into force of these Regulations.

(b)   The installation of lights with colour specifications as prescribed in Section 7 of Annex I to these Regulations, until 4 years after the date of entry into force of these Regulations.

(c)   The repositioning of lights as a result of conversion from Imperial to metric units and rounding off measurement figures, permanent exemption.

(d)   (i)   The repositioning of masthead lights on vessels of less than 150 metres in length, resulting from the prescriptions of Section 3(a) of Annex I to these Regulations, permanent exemption.

    (ii)   The repositioning of masthead lights on vessels of 150 metres or more in length, resulting from the prescriptions of Section 3(a) of Annex I to these Regulations, until 9 years after the date of entry into force of these Regulations.

(a)   See Cmnd.2956 and Schedule 1 to the Collision Regulations (Ships and Seaplanes on the Water) and Signals of Distress (Ships) Order 1965 (S.I. 1965/1525)

(e)   The repositioning of masthead lights resulting from the prescriptions of Section 2(b) of Annex I to these Regulations, until 9 years after the date of entry into force of these Regulations.

(f)   The repositioning of sidelights resulting from the prescriptions of Sections 2(g) and 3(b) of Annex I to these Regulations, until 9 years after the date of entry into force of these Regulations.

(g)   The requirements for sound signal appliances prescribed in Annex III to these Regulations, until 9 years after the date of entry into force of these Regulations.

(h)   The repositioning of all-round lights resulting from the prescription of Section 9(b) of Annex I to these Regulations, permanent exemption.

ANNEX I

Positioning and technical details of lights and shapes

1.   *Definition*

The term "height above the hull" means height above the uppermost continuous deck. This height shall be measured from the position vertically beneath the location of the light.

2.   *Vertical positioning and spacing of lights*

(a)   On a power-driven vessel of 20 metres or more in length the masthead lights shall be placed as follows:

     (i)   the forward masthead light, or if only one masthead light is carried, then that light, at a height above the hull of not less than 6 metres, and, if the breadth of the vessel exceeds 6 metres, then at a height above the hull not less than such breadth, so however that the light need not be placed at a greater height above the hull than 12 metres;

     (ii)   when two masthead lights are carried the after one shall be at least 4.5 metres vertically higher than the forward one.

(b)   The vertical separation of masthead lights of power-driven vessels shall be such that in all normal conditions of trim the after light will be seen over and separate from the forward light at a distance of 1,000 metres from the stem when viewed from sea-level.

(c)   The masthead light of a power-driven vessel of 12 metres but less than 20 metres in length shall be placed at a height above the gunwale of not less than 2.5 metres.

(d)   A power-driven vessel of less than 12 metres in length may carry the uppermost light at a height of less than 2.5 metres above the gunwale. When however a masthead light is carried in addition to sidelights and a sternlight or the all-round light prescribed in Rule 23(c)(i) is carried in addition to sidelights, then such masthead light or all-round light shall be carried at least 1 metre higher than the sidelights.

(e)   One of the two or three masthead lights prescribed for a power-driven vessel when engaged in towing or pushing another vessel shall be placed in the same position as either the forward masthead light or the after masthead light; provided that, if carried on the aftermast, the lowest after masthead light shall be at least 4.5 metres vertically higher than the forward masthead light.

(f) (i) The masthead light or lights prescribed in Rule 23(a) shall be so placed as to be above and clear of all other lights and obstructions except as described in sub-paragraph (ii).

(ii) When it is impracticable to carry the all-round lights prescribed by Rule 27(b)(i) or Rule 28 below the masthead lights, they may be carried above the after masthead light(s) or vertically in between the forward masthead light(s) and the after masthead light(s) provided that in the latter case the requirement of Section 3(c) of this Annex shall be complied with.

(g) The sidelights of a power-driven vessel shall be placed at a height above the hull not greater than three-quarters of that of the forward masthead light. They shall not be so low as to be interfered with by deck lights.

(h) The sidelights, if in a combined lantern and carried on a power-driven vessel of less than 20 metres in length, shall be placed not less than 1 metre below the masthead light.

(i) When the Rules prescribe two or three lights to be carried in a vertical line, they shall be spaced as follows:

(i) on a vessel of 20 metres in length or more such lights shall be spaced not less than 2 metres apart, and the lowest of these lights shall, except where a towing light is required, be placed at a height of not less than 4 metres above the hull;

(ii) on a vessel of less than 20 metres in length such lights shall be spaced not less than 1 metre apart and the lowest of these lights shall, except where a towing light is required, be placed at a height of not less than 2 metres above the gunwale;

(iii) when three lights are carried they shall be equally spaced.

(j) The lower of the two all-round lights prescribed for a vessel when engaged in fishing shall be at a height above the sidelights not less than twice the distance between the two vertical lights.

(k) The forward anchor light prescribed in Rule 30(a)(i), when two are carried, shall not be less than 4.5 metres above the after one. On a vessel of 50 metres or more in length this forward anchor light shall be placed at a height of not less than 6 metres above the hull.

3. *Horizontal positioning and spacing of lights*

(a) When two masthead lights are prescribed for a power-driven vessel, the horizontal distance between them shall not be less than one-half of the length of the vessel but need not be more than 100 metres. The forward light shall be placed not more than one-quarter of the length of the vessel from the stem.

(b) On a power-driven vessel of 20 metres or more in length the sidelights shall not be placed in front of the forward masthead lights. They shall be placed at or near the side of the vessel.

(c) When the lights prescribed in Rule 27(b)(i) or Rule 28 are placed vertically between the forward masthead light(s) and the after masthead light(s) these all-round lights shall be placed at a horizontal distance of not less than 2 metres from the fore and aft centreline of the vessels in the athwartship direction.

(d) When only one masthead light is prescribed for a power-driven vessel, this light shall be exhibited forward of amidships; except that a vessel of less than 20 metres in length need not exhibit this light forward of amidships but shall exhibit it as far forward as is practicable.

4. *Details of location of direction-indicating lights for fishing vessels, dredgers and vessels engaged in underwater operations*

(a)   The light indicating the direction of the outlying gear from a vessel engaged in fishing as prescribed in Rule 26(c)(ii). shall be placed at a horizontal distance of not less than 2 metres and not more than 6 metres away from the two all-round red and white lights. This light shall be placed not higher than the all-round white light prescribed in Rule 26(c)(i) and not lower than the sidelights.

(b)   The lights and shapes on a vessel engaged in dredging or underwater operations to indicate the obstructed side and or the side on which it is safe to pass, as prescribed in Rule 27(d)(i) and (ii), shall be placed at the maximum practical horizontal distance, but in no case less than 2 metres, from the lights or shapes prescribed in Rule 27(b)(i) and (ii). In no case shall the upper of these lights or shapes be at a greater height than the lower of the three lights or shapes prescribed in Rule 27(b)(i) and (ii).

5.   *Screens for sidelights*

The sidelights of vessels of 20 metres or more in length shall be fitted with inboard screens painted matt black, and meeting the requirements of Section 9 of this Annex. On vessels of less than 20 metres in length the sidelights, if necessary to meet the requirements of Section 9 of this Annex, shall be fitted with inboard matt black screens. With a combined lantern, using a single vertical filament and a very narrow division between the green and red sections, external screens need not be fitted.

6.   *Shapes*

(a)   Shapes shall be black and of the following sizes:

(i)   a ball shall have a diameter of not less than 0.6 metre;

(ii)   a cone shall have a base diameter of not less than 0.6 metre and a height equal to its diameter;

(iii)   a cylinder shall have a diameter of at least 0.6 metre and a height of twice its diameter

(iv)   a diamond shape shall consist of two cones as defined in (ii) above having a common base.

(b)   The vertical distance between shapes shall be at least 1.5 metres.

(c)   In a vessel of less than 20 metres in length shapes of lesser dimensions but commensurate with the size of the vessel may be used and the distance apart may be correspondingly reduced.

7.   *Colour specification of lights*

The chromaticity of all navigation lights shall conform to the following standards, which lie within the boundaries of the area of the diagram specified for each colour by the International Commission on Illumination (CIE).

The boundaries of the area for each colour are given by indicating the corner co-ordinates, which are as follows:

(i)   White

x	0.525	0.525	0.452	0.310	0.310	0.443
y	0.382	0.440	0.440	0.348	0.283	0.382

(ii)   Green

x	0.028	0.009	0.300	0.203
y	0.385	0.723	0.511	0.356

(iii)   Red

x	0.680	0.660	0.735	0.721
y	0.320	0.320	0.265	0.259

(iv)   Yellow

x	0.612	0.618	0.575	0.575
y	0.382	0.382	0.425	0.406

8.   *Intensity of lights*

(a)   The minimum luminous intensity of lights shall be calculated by using

$$I = 3.43 \times 10^6 \times T \times D^2 \times K^{-D}$$

where   I   is luminous intensity in candelas under service conditions,

        T   is threshold factor 2×10^{-7} lux,

        D   is range of visibility (luminous range) of the light in nautical miles,

        K   is atmospheric transmissivity.

For prescribed lights the value of K shall be 0.8, corresponding to a meteorological visibility of approximately 13 nautical miles.

(b)   A selection of figures derived from the formula is given in the following table:

Range of visibility (luminous range) of light in nautical miles D	Luminous intensity of light in candelas for K=0.8 I
1	0.9
2	4.3
3	12
4	27
5	52
6	94

Note: The maximum luminous intensity of navigation lights should be limited to avoid undue glare. This shall not be achieved by a variable control of the luminous intensity.

9. *Horizontal sectors*

(a) (i) In the forward direction, sidelights as fitted on the vessel shall show the minimum required intensities. The intensities shall decrease to reach practical cut-off between 1 degree and 3 degrees outside the prescribed sectors.

(ii) For stern lights and masthead lights at 22.5 degrees abaft the beam for sidelights, the minimum required intensities shall be maintained over the arc of the horizon up to 5 degrees within the limits of the sectors prescribed in Rule 21. From 5 degrees within the prescribed sectors the intensity may decrease by 50 per cent up to the prescribed limits: it shall decrease steadily to reach practical cut-off at not more than 5 degrees outside the prescribed sectors.

(b) (i) All-round lights shall be so located as not to be obscured by masts, topmasts or structures within angular sectors of more than 6 degrees, except anchor lights prescribed in Rule 30, which need not be placed at an impracticable height above the hull.

(ii) If it is impracticable to comply with paragraph (b) (i) of this section by exhibiting only one all-round light, two all-round lights shall be used suitably positioned or screened so that they appear, as far as practicable, as one light at a distance of one mile.

10. *Vertical sectors*

(a) The vertical sectors of electric lights as fitted, with the exception of lights on sailing vessels underway shall ensure that:

(i) at least the required minimum intensity is maintained at all angles from 5 degrees above to 5 degrees below the horizontal;

(ii) at least 60 per cent of the required minimum intensity is maintained from 7.5 degrees above to 7.5 degrees below the horizontal.

(b) In the case of sailing vessels underway the vertical sectors of electric lights as fitted shall ensure that:

(i) at least the required minimum intensity is maintained at all angles from 5 degrees above to 5 degrees below the horizontal;

(ii) at least 50 per cent of the required minimum intensity is maintained from 25 degrees above to 25 degrees below the horizontal.

(c) In the case of lights other than electric these specifications shall be met as closely as possible.

11. *Intensity of non-electric lights*

Non-electric lights shall so far as practicable comply with the minimum intensities, as specified in the table given in Section 8 of this Annex.

12. *Manoeuvring light*

Notwithstanding the provisions of paragraph 2(f) of this Annex the manoeuvring light described in Rule 34(b) shall be placed in the same fore and aft vertical plane as the masthead light or lights and, where practicable, at a minimum height of 2 metres vertically above the forward masthead light, provided that it shall be carried not less than 2 metres vertically above or below the after masthead light. On a vessel where only one masthead light is carried the manoeuvring light, if fitted, shall be carried where it can best be seen, not less than 2 metres vertically apart from the masthead light.

13. **High Speed Craft***

(a) The masthead light of high-speed craft may be placed at a height related to the breadth of the lower than that prescribed in paragraph 2(a)(i) of this annex, provided that the base angle of the isosceles triangles formed by the sidelights and masthead light, when seen in end elevation, is not less than 27°.

(b) On high-speed craft of 50 metres or more in length, the vertical separation between foremast and mainmast light of 4.5 metres required by paragraph 2(a)(ii) of this annex may be modified provided that such distance shall not be less than the value determined by the following formula:

$$Y = \frac{(a + 17\Psi)}{1000} C + 2$$

Where: y is the height of the mainmast light above the foremast light in metres;
A is the height of the foremast light above the water surface in service condition in metres;
C is the trim in service condition in degrees;
C is the horizontal separation of masthead lights in metres.

* Refer to the International Code of Safety for High-Speed Craft, 1994 and the International Code of Safety for High-Speed Craft, 2000.

14. *Approval*

The construction of lights and shapes and the installation of lights on board the vessel shall be to the satisfaction of the appropriate authority of the State whose flag the vessel is entitled to fly.

ANNEX II

Additional signals for fishing vessels fishing in close proximity

1. *General*

The lights mentioned herein shall, if exhibited in pursuance of Rule 26(d), be placed where they can best be seen. They shall be at least 0.9 metre apart but at a lower level than lights prescribed in Rule 26(b)(i) and (c)(i). The lights shall be visible all round the horizon at a distance of at least 1 mile but at a lesser distance than the lights prescribed by these Rules for fishing vessels.

2. *Signals for trawlers*

(a)   Vessels of 20 metres or more in length when engaged in trawling, whether using demersal or pelagic gear, shall exhibit:

  (i)   when shooting their nets, two white lights in a vertical line;

  (ii)   when hauling their nets, one white light over one red light in a vertical line;

  (iii)   when the net has come fast upon an obstruction, two red lights in a vertical line.

(b)   Each vessel of 20 metres or more in length engaged in pair trawling shall exhibit:

  (i)   by night, a searchlight directed forward and in the direction of the other vessel of the pair;

  (ii)   when shooting or hauling their nets or when the nets have come fast upon an obstruction, the lights prescribed in 2(a) above.

  (c)   A vessel of less than 20 metres in length engaged in trawling, whether using demersal or pelagic gear or engaged in pair trawling, may exhibit the lights prescribed in paragraphs (a) or (b) of this Section, as appropriate.

3. *Signals for purse seiners*

Vessels engaged in fishing with purse seine gear may exhibit two yellow lights in a vertical line. These lights shall flash alternately every second and with equal light and occultation duration. These lights may be exhibited only when the vessel is hampered by its fishing gear.

ANNEX III

Technical details of sound signal appliances

1. *Whistles*

(a) *Frequencies and range of audibility*

The fundamental frequency of the signal shall lie within the range 70 - 700 Hz. The range of audibility of the signal from a whistle shall be determined by those frequencies, which may include the fundamental and/or one or more higher frequencies, which lie within the range 180 - 700 Hz (+/-1%) for a vessel of 20 metres or more in length, or 180-2100Hz (+/-1%) for a vessel of less than 20 metres in length and which provide the sound pressure levels specified in paragraph 1(c) below.

(b)   *Limits of fundamental frequencies*

To ensure a wide variety of whistle characteristics, the fundamental frequency of a whistle shall be between the following limits:

(i)   70 - 200 Hz, for a vessel 200 metres or more in length;
(ii)   130 - 350 Hz, for a vessel 75 metres but less than 200 metres in length;
(iii) 250 - 700 Hz, for a vessel less than 75 metres in length.

(c)   *Sound signal intensity and range of audibility*

A whistle fitted in a vessel shall provide, in the direction of maximum intensity of the whistle and at a distance of 1 metre from it, a sound pressure level in at least one 1/3rd-octave band within the range of frequencies 180 - 700 Hz (+/-1%) for a vessel of 20 metres or more in length, or 180-2100Hz (+/-1%) for a vessel of less than 20 metres in length, of not less than the appropriate figure given in the table below.

Length of vessel in metres	1/3rd-octave band level at 1 metre in dB referred to $2x10^{-5}N/m^2$	Audibility range in nautical miles
200 or more	143	2
75 but less than 200	138	1.5
20 but less than 75	130	1
Less than 20	120 *	0.5
	115 †	
	111 ‡	

* When the measured frequencies lie within the range 180-450Hz
† When the measured frequencies lie within the range 450-800Hz
‡ When the measured frequencies lie within the range 800-2100Hz

The range of audibility in the table above is for information and is approximately the range at which a whistle may be heard on its forward axis with 90 per cent probability in conditions of still air on board a vessel having average background noise level at the listening posts (taken to be 68 dB in the octave band centered on 250 Hz and 63 dB in the octave band centered on 500Hz.

In practice the range at which a whistle may be heard is extremely variable and depends critically on weather conditions; the values given can be regarded as typical but under conditions of strong wind or high ambient noise level at the listening post the range may be much reduced.

d)   *Directional Properties*

The sound pressure level of a directional whistle shall be not more than 4 dB below the prescribed sound pressure level on the axis at any direction in the horizontal plane within ±45 degrees of the axis. The sound pressure level at any other direction in the horizontal plane shall be not more than 10 dB below the prescribed sound pressure level on the axis, so that the range in any direction will be at least half the range on the forward axis. The sound pressure level shall be measured in that 1/3rd-octave band which determines the audibility range.

(e)   Positioning of whistles

When a directional whistle is to be used as the only whistle on a vessel, it shall be installed with its maximum intensity directed straight ahead.

A whistle shall be placed as high as practicable on a vessel, in order to reduce interception of the emitted sound by obstructions and also to minimize hearing damage risk to personnel. The sound pressure level of the vessel's own signal at listening posts shall not exceed 110 dB (A) and so far as practicable should not exceed 100 dB (A).

(f)   Fitting of more than one whistle

If whistles are fitted at a distance apart of more than 100 metres, it shall be so arranged that they are not sounded simultaneously.

(g)   Combined whistle systems

If due to the presence of obstructions the sound field of a single whistle or one of the whistles referred to in paragraph 1(f) above is likely to have a zone of greatly reduced signal level, it is recommended that a combined whistle system be fitted so as to overcome this reduction. For the purposes of the Rules a combined whistle system is to be regarded as a single whistle. The whistles of a combined system shall be located at a distance apart of not more than 100 metres and arranged to be sounded simultaneously. The frequency of any one whistle shall differ from those of the others by at least 10 Hz.

2.   Bell or gong

(a)   Intensity of signal

A bell or gong, or other device having similar sound characteristics shall produce a sound pressure level of not less than 110 dB at a distance of 1 metre from it.

(b)   Construction

Bells and gongs shall be made of corrosion-resistant material and designed to give a clear tone. The diameter of the mouth of the bell shall be not less than 300 mm for vessels of 20 metres or more in length. Where practicable, a power-driven bell striker is recommended to ensure constant force but manual operation shall be possible. The mass of the striker shall be not less than 3 per cent of the mass of the bell.

3.   Approval

The construction of sound signal appliances, their performance and their installation on board the vessel shall be to the satisfaction of the appropriate authority of the State whose flag the vessel is entitled to fly.

ANNEX IV

Distress signals

1.   The following signals, used or exhibited either together or separately, indicate distress and need of assistance:

(a)   a gun or other explosive signal fired at intervals of about a minute;

(b)   a continuous sounding with any fog-signalling apparatus;

(c)   rockets or shells, throwing red stars fired one at a time at short intervals;

(d)   a signal made by radiotelegraphy or by any other signalling method consisting of the group $\cdots---\cdots$ (SOS) in the Morse Code;

(e)   a signal sent by radiotelephony consisting of the spoken word "Mayday";

(f)   the International Code Signal of distress indicated by N.C.;

(g)   a signal consisting of a square flag having above or below it a ball anything resembling a ball;

(h)   flames on the vessel (as from a burning tar barrel, oil barrel, etc.);

(i)   a rocket parachute flare or a hand flare showing a red light;

(j)   a smoke signal giving off orange-coloured smoke;

(k)   slowly and repeatedly raising and lowering arms outstretched to each side;

(l)   the radiotelegraph alarm signal;

(m)   the radiotelephone alarm signal;

(n)   signals transmitted by emergency position-indicating radio beacons;

(o)   approved signals transmitted by radiocommunication systems, including survival craft radar transponders.

2.   The use or exhibition of any of the foregoing signals except for the purpose of indicating distress and need of assistance and the use of other signals which may be confused with any of the above signals is prohibited.

3.   Attention is drawn to the relevant sections of the International Code of Signals, the Merchant Ship Search and Rescue Manual and the following signals:

(a)   a piece of orange-coloured canvas with either a black square and circle or other appropriate symbol (for identification from the air);

(b)   a dye marker.

MERCHANT SHIPPING NOTICE

Maritime and Coastguard Agency

MSN 1781 (M+F)
(Amendment)

The Merchant Shipping (Distress Signals and Prevention of Collisions) Regulations 1996 - Amendments to Annex IV (Distress Signals)

Notice to all Owners, Masters, Skippers, Officers and Crews of Merchant Ships, Fishing Vessels, Pleasure Vessels, Yachts and Other Seagoing Craft.

This notice should be read in conjunction with MSN 1781 (M+F) as amended

---

PLEASE NOTE:-
Where this document provides guidance on the law it should not be regarded as definitive. The way the law applies to any particular case can vary according to circumstances - for example, from vessel to vessel and you should consider seeking independent legal advice if you are unsure of your own legal position.

Summary

- This notice details amendments to Annex IV of the Convention on the International Regulations for Preventing Collisions at Sea, 1972 (COLREGs). These amendments have been adopted by the International Maritime Organisation's(IMO) Maritime Safety Committee (MSC) and will come into force in the United Kingdom on 1 December 2009.

1. Introduction

1.1 International Regulations for Preventing Collisions at Sea, 1972(COLREGS) Convention is given legal effect in United Kingdom legislation through the Merchant Shipping (Distress Signals and Prevention of Collisions) Regulations 1996 (SI 1996 No.75).

1.2 The amendments in this notice relate to three sets of changes to Section 1 of Annex IV of the Regulations for Preventing Collisions at Sea, 1972 which were adopted by the IMO Maritime Safety Committee at its 82nd session came into force for implementation in the United Kingdom on 1 December 2009.

2. Amendments to Annex IV of International Regulations for Preventing Collisions at Sea, 1972, as amended (COLREGs), arising from IMO Resolution A. 1004 (25), adopted on 29 November 2007 which result in revisions to MSN 1781 (M+F) as amended.

ANNEX

AMENDMENTS TO THE INTERNATIONAL REGULATIONS FOR PREVENTING COLLISIONS AT SEA, 1972, AS AMENDED

Annex IV

Distress signals

1 The following signals, used or exhibited either together or separately, indicate distress and need of assistance:

(a) a gun or other explosive signals fired at intervals of about a minute;
(b) a continuous sounding with any fog-signalling apparatus;
(c) rockets or shells, throwing red stars fired one at a time at short intervals;
(d) **a signal made by any signalling method consisting of the group ... --- ... (SOS) in the Morse Code;**
(e) a signal sent by radiotelephony consisting of the spoken word .MAYDAY.;
(f) the International Code Signal of distress indicated by N.C.;
(g) a signal consisting of a square flag having above or below it a ball or anything resembling a ball;
(h) flames on the vessel (as from a burning tar barrel, oil barrel, etc.);
(i) a rocket parachute flare or a hand-flare showing a red light;
(j) a smoke signal giving off orange-coloured smoke;
(k) slowly and repeatedly raising and lowering arms outstretched to each side;
(l) **a distress alert by means of digital selective calling (DSC) transmitted on:**
   (i) VHF channel 70, or
   (ii) MF/HF on the frequencies 2187.5 kHz, 8414.5 kHz, 4207.5 kHz, 6312 kHz, 12577 kHz or 16804.5 kHz;
(m) **a ship-to-shore distress alert transmitted by the ship's Inmarsat or other mobile satellite service provider ship earth station;**
(n) signals transmitted by emergency position-indicating radio beacons;
(o) approved signals transmitted by radiocommunications systems, including survival craft radar transponders.

2 The use or exhibition of any of the foregoing signals, except for the purpose of indicating distress and need of assistance and the use of other signals which may be confused with any of the above signals, is prohibited.

3 Attention is drawn to the relevant sections of the International Code of Signals, the International Aeronautical and Maritime Search and Rescue Manual, Volume III and the following signals:
(a) a piece of orange-coloured canvas with either a black square and circle or other appropriate symbol (for identification from the air);
(b) a dye marker.

More Information

Navigation Safety Branch

Maritime and Coastguard Agency
Bay 2/4
Spring Place
105 Commercial Road
Southampton
SO15 1EG

Tel :	+44 (0) 23 8032 9316
Fax :	+44 (0) 23 8032 9204
e-mail:	navemails@mcga.gov.uk

General Inquiries: 24 Hour Infoline
                       infoline@mcga.gov.uk
                       0870 600 6505

MCA Website Address: www.mcga.gov.uk

File Ref:

Published: Printers to Insert [Month Year]

© Crown Copyright 2006

Safer Lives, Safer Ships, Cleaner Seas

Printed on material containing minimum 75% post-consumer waste paper

GB06/68827.00

An executive agency of the
Department for
Transport

mca
Maritime and Coastguard Agency

MGN 40 (M)

International Safety Management (ISM) Code

Notice to Shipowners, Ship Operators, Charterers and Managers; Ship's Masters,
Ship's Officers and Seamen.

This Note supersedes M1353, M1424 and M1616.

Summary

This note informs ship operators and crews about the ISM Code.

Key Points:

- Introduction of new Merchant Shipping Regulations.
- Brief introduction to the ISM Code.
- Ships to which the Code applies and the applicable dates.
- Voluntary Certification scheme.
- Advice and useful references.

INTRODUCTION

1. The purpose of this Marine Guidance Note is to introduce the proposed Merchant Shipping Regulations, give a brief introduction to the ISM Code, explain to which vessels it will apply and the date by which, according to vessel type, the Code becomes mandatory. This note also sets out the Maritime and Coastguard Agency's voluntary certification scheme and gives advice and some useful references on good ship management practice.

2. The International Management Code for the Safe Operation of Ships and for Pollution Prevention (ISM Code) was made mandatory in 1994 by the adoption of Chapter IX to SOLAS[1] '74, which will be implemented in UK law by the proposed Merchant Shipping (International Safety

Management (ISM) Code) Regulations 1998 which are due to come into force on 1 July 1998. A copy of the annex to IMO Resolution A.741(18), which constitutes the ISM Code, is reproduced as Annex 1 to this Note.

3. Merchant shipping operations are inherently complex and governed by national and international rules and conventions largely addressing technical aspects. This technical control can achieve only part of the objectives of safe and pollution free ship operations. The Master is clearly responsible for the safety of the ship and its crew but the overall responsibility for the administration and safe operation rests with the company or person(s) owning or managing the ship.

4. It is widely accepted that the vast majority of shipping accidents are attributable to human error and it is generally agreed that the human element plays some part in virtually all accidents. Therefore the task facing all ship operating companies is to

---

[1] SOLAS: International Convention for the Safety of Life at Sea, 1974.

minimise the scope for poor or incorrect decisions which contribute directly, or indirectly, to a casualty or pollution incident. Every action affecting safety or pollution prevention at any level in a company must be based on sound organisational practices.

5. The ISM Code sets an international standard for the safe management and operation of ships and requires companies to document and implement clear procedures, standards and instructions for safety management ashore and afloat. Guidance on developing a Safety Management System, including some useful references, to meet the requirements of the Code is given in Annex 2 to this Note.

6. *The Designated Person:* The MCA considers the designated person's role to be highly important and expects companies to regard it in the same light and to consequently provide the necessary responsibility, authority and resources. The regulations do not state who it should be or what qualifications they must have, but they should be well experienced in the operation of ships both at sea and in port. It is essential that the person must have direct access to the highest level of management in the company.

7. The ISM Code does **NOT** replace the requirement for compliance with existing regulations.

MANDATORY IMPLEMENTATION

8. The Code is being introduced on a mandatory basis in four stages, dependent on vessel type but regardless of the date of construction.

9. **European Requirements**

   9.1 The Merchant Shipping (ISM Code) (Ro-Ro Passenger Ferries) Regulations 1997 implement in UK law the European Council Regulation[2] on the Safety Management of Ro-Ro Passenger Vessels. The EC Regulation entered into force on 1 January 1996

---

[2] Council Regulation (EC) No. 3051/95 of 8 December 1995.

and has been applicable to sea going passenger roll-on/roll-off ferries operating a regular service to or from a port of a Member State of the European Community, regardless of the vessel's flag, since **1 July 1996.**

   9.2 By way of derogation, companies operating ro-ro ferries on a regular service exclusively in sheltered waters between ports in the same Member State were permitted to defer compliance until **1 July 1997.**

10. **International Requirements:** The new Chapter IX to SOLAS '74, Management for the Safe Operation of Ships, which is to be implemented in UK law by Merchant Shipping (International Safety Management (ISM) Code) Regulations (due to come into force on 1 July 1998), makes provision for the mandatory enforcement of the ISM Code on ships engaged on international voyages and is applicable as follows:

   .1 Passenger ships, including passenger high speed craft, (although some, as detailed under paragraph 9 above, will already comply) are required to comply not later than **1 July 1998.**

   .2 Oil tankers, chemical tankers, gas carriers, bulk carriers and cargo high speed craft all of 500 GT and over, are also required to comply not later than **1 July 1998.**

   .3 Other cargo ships and mobile offshore drilling units all of 500 GT and over, are required to comply not later than **1 July 2002.**

11. The proposed Merchant Shipping (International Safety Management (ISM) Code) Regulations will revoke the Merchant Shipping (Operations Book) Regulations 1988 which applied to Class II and II(A) vessels. The new regulations will also be applicable to vessels of Class II(A) in addition to those vessels engaged on international voyages required by the SOLAS Convention.

12. The MCA will be responsible for verifying compliance with the ISM Code both ashore and afloat, will issue ISM Convention Certificates and will carry out periodic

verification and certificate renewal. The use of independent organisations to guide and assist in the setting up of Safety Management Systems is encouraged but the choice of such organisations is a company decision.

VOLUNTARY IMPLEMENTATION

13. Chapter IX of SOLAS '74, which makes the ISM Code mandatory, applies to cargo ships of 500 GT and over and thus excludes a significant number of ships of less than 500 GT from the application of that chapter. It is recognised that there is a need for the proper organisation of management to achieve and maintain high standards of safety and environmental protection by all those involved in the operation of ships, even if less than 500 GT. Therefore, the UK strongly urges companies operating ships of between 150 GT and 500 GT to comply with the requirements of the ISM Code and to apply for certification voluntarily.

CERTIFICATION

14. The application of the Code will lead to the issue of two statutory certificates which will be subject to Port State Control inspections under regulation XI/4 of SOLAS '74. Vessels without the required certificates are liable to be detained and at least within Europe (Paris MOU region) may be banned from re-entry until compliance has been adequately demonstrated. The two certificates, which for the purposes of port state control are treated as certificates issued under regulation I/12 or I/13 of SOLAS, are the Document of Compliance (DOC) and the Safety Management Certificate (SMC).

15. **The Document of Compliance (DOC)**

    15.1 The DOC will be issued to the company following a successful audit of the shore side aspects of the Safety Management System. The audit will require objective evidence to demonstrate that the system has been in operation for a minimum of three months[3] in addition to similar evidence of operation on at least one ship of each type in the company fleet.

The DOC will be specific to ship type(s) at the time of the audit, valid for a maximum of five years and subject to annual verification (± 3 months of the anniversary date).

15.2 An interim DOC (valid for a maximum of 12 months) may be issued to facilitate initial implementation of the ISM Code where a company is newly established or where new ship types are added to an existing DOC. The interim DOC will only be issued following a demonstration from the Company that it has a SMS that meets the objectives of 1.2.3 of the ISM Code. The Company must demonstrate plans to implement a SMS meeting the full requirements of the Code.

16. **The Safety Management Certificate (SMC)**

    16.1 The SMC will be issued to each individual ship after an on board audit of the SMS. Objective evidence will be required to demonstrate that the SMS has been in operation on board the ship for a minimum of three months[3] before the audit. The company must be in possession of a valid DOC, a certified true copy of which must be on board the ships. The SMC will be valid for a maximum of five years and will be subject to one intermediate verification between the second and third anniversaries, with the proviso that more frequent audits, if deemed necessary by the MCA, may be carried out. This is considered more likely in the early days of ISM Code implementation.

    16.2 An interim SMC, valid for not more than six months, may be issued to new ships on delivery and when a company takes on the responsibility for the management of a ship which is new to the company.

APPLICATION

17. The MCA will, in general, deal with requests for verification in order of application.

18. For those ships not legally required to comply with the Code, voluntary certification is strongly urged, but priority

---

[3] The qualifying periods can be concurrent.

will be given to those companies where compliance is mandatory.

19. Applications received late may not be dealt with in time for the relevant Certificates to be issued. Applications received well in advance of the required dates (e.g. an application for compliance not required before 2002) will not be refused but priority may need to be given to those with the more urgent need.

20. **AUDIT - APPLICATION AND CONDUCT**

Applications may be made as follows:

.1 **For the DOC** - by letter to the MCA at the following address:

The Audit Section, MSAS(D)
Maritime and Coastguard Agency
Spring Place
105 Commercial Road
SOUTHAMPTON
SO15 1EG
Tel: 01703 329202

The Audit Section will respond and request a Document review either on site or by despatch of Documents to the MCA Where the Document review is carried out is generally a company choice. An audit plan and timetable will be agreed. The company will then be audited and, dependent on the result, a Document of Compliance issued.

.2 **For the SMC** - for audit of individual ships to the relevant Marine Office of the MCA.

21. The audit and inspection will be conducted in accordance with MCA Instructions to Surveyors which are under development at the present time and in cognisance of IMO Guidelines. In certain instances, where for example a vessel rarely calls at a UK port, the MCA may appoint a Surveyor to act on its behalf. Such arrangements will be conducted in accordance with current practice.

22. **Multi-Flag Fleets:** For UK flagged ships operated by companies whose DOC has been issued by or on behalf of another flag Administration, companies are requested to follow the Guidance given in the Annex to IMO MSC/Circular 762, attached at Annex 3 to this Note. Paragraph 5 is particularly worthy of note as it states companies should approach the relevant flag Administrations, proposing a plan of action and requesting agreement by all parties.

FEES

23. The fees charged for audit against the ISM Code will be based on the time taken by surveyors to complete all aspects of the work at the hourly fee rate current at the time.

MSAS(D)
Maritime and Coastguard Agency
Spring Place
105 Commercial Road
Southampton
SO15 1 EG

Tel: 01703 329202
Fax: 01703 329379

April 1998

MS 166/2/5

© Crown Copyright 1998

DETR
ENVIRONMENT
TRANSPORT
REGIONS

An executive agency of the Department of the Enviroment, Transport and the Regions

ANNEX 1: ISM CODE

Annex to IMO Resolution A.741(18)
Adopted on 4 November 1993

INTERNATIONAL MANAGEMENT CODE FOR THE SAFE OPERATION OF SHIPS AND FOR POLLUTION PREVENTION (INTERNATIONAL SAFETY MANAGEMENT (ISM) CODE)

SAFETY AND POLLUTION PREVENTION MANAGEMENT REQUIREMENTS

CONTENTS

PREAMBLE

1 The purpose of this Code is to provide an international standard for the safe management and operation of ships and for pollution prevention.

2 The Assembly adopted resolution A.443(XI) by which it invited all Governments to take the necessary steps to safeguard the shipmaster in the proper discharge of his responsibilities with regard to maritime safety and the protection of the marine environment.

3 The Assembly also adopted resolution A.680(17) by which it further recognised the need for appropriate organisation of management to enable it to respond to the need of those on board ships to achieve and maintain high standards of safety and environmental protection.

4 Recognising that no two shipping companies or shipowners are the same, and that ships operate under a wide range of different conditions, the Code is based on general principles and objectives.

5 The Code is expressed in broad terms so that it can have a widespread application. Clearly, different levels of management, whether shore-based or at sea, will require varying levels of knowledge and awareness of the items outlined.

6 The cornerstone of good safety management is commitment from the top. In matters of safety and pollution prevention it is the commitment, competence, attitudes and motivation of individuals at all levels that determines the end result.

1 GENERAL

1.1 Definitions

1.1.1 "International Safety Management (ISM) Code" means the International Management Code for the Safe Operation of Ships and for Pollution Prevention as adopted by the Assembly, as may be amended by the Organisation.

1.1.2 "Company" means the Owner of the ship or any other organisation or person such as the Manager, or the Bareboat Charterer, who has assumed the responsibility for operation of the ship from the Shipowner and who on assuming such responsibility has agreed to take over all the duties and responsibility imposed by the Code.

1.1.3 "Administration" means the Government of the State whose flag the ship is entitled to fly.

1.2 Objectives

1.2.1 The objectives of the Code are to ensure safety at sea, prevention of human injury or loss of life, and avoidance of damage to the environment, in particular, to the marine environment, and to property.

1.2.2 Safety management objectives of the Company should, <u>inter alia</u>:

.1 provide for safe practices in ship operation and a safe working environment;

.2 establish safeguards against all identified risks; and

.3 continuously improve safety management skills of personnel ashore and aboard ships, including preparation for emergencies related both to safety and environmental protection.

1.2.3 The safety management system should ensure:

.1 compliance with mandatory rules and regulations; and

.2 that applicable codes, guidelines and standards recommended by the Organisation, Administrations, classification societies and maritime industry organisations are taken into account.

1.3 Application

The requirements of this Code may be applied to all ships.

1.4 Functional requirements for a Safety Management System (SMS)

Every Company should develop, implement and maintain a Safety Management System (SMS) which includes the following functional requirements:

.1 a safety and environmental protection policy;

.2 instructions and procedures to ensure safe operation of ships and protection of the environment in compliance with relevant international and flag state legislation;

.3 defined levels of authority and lines of communication between, and amongst, shore and shipboard personnel;

.4 procedures for reporting accidents and non-conformities with the provisions of this Code;

.5 procedures to prepare for and respond to emergency situations; and

.6 procedures for internal audits and management reviews.

2 SAFETY AND ENVIRONMENTAL PROTECTION POLICY

2.1 The Company should establish a safety and environmental protection policy which describes how the objectives, given in paragraph 1.2, will be achieved.

2.2 The Company should ensure that the policy is implemented and maintained at all levels of the organisation both ship based and shore based.

3 COMPANY RESPONSIBILITIES AND AUTHORITY

3.1 If the entity who is responsible for the operation of the ship is other than the owner, the owner must report the full name and details of such entity to the Administration.

3.2 The Company should define and document the responsibility, authority and interrelation of all personnel who manage, perform and verify work relating to and affecting safety and pollution prevention.

3.3 The Company is responsible for ensuring that adequate resources and shore based support are provided to enable the designated person or persons to carry out their functions.

4 DESIGNATED PERSON(S)

To ensure the safe operation of each ship and to provide a link between the Company and those on board, every Company, as appropriate, should designate a person or persons ashore having direct access to the highest level of management. The responsibility and authority of the designated person or persons should include monitoring the safety and pollution prevention aspects of the operation of each ship and ensuring that adequate resources and shore based support are applied, as required.

5 MASTER'S RESPONSIBILITY AND AUTHORITY

5.1 The Company should clearly define and document the master's responsibility with regard to:

.1 implementing the safety and environmental-protection policy of the Company;

.2 motivating the crew in the observation of that policy;

.3 issuing appropriate orders and instructions in a clear and simple manner;

.4 verifying that specified requirements are observed; and

.5 reviewing the SMS and reporting its deficiencies to the shore-based management.

5.2 The Company should ensure that the SMS operating on board the ship contains a clear statement emphasising the master's authority. The Company should establish in the SMS that the master has the overriding authority and the responsibility to make decisions with respect to safety and pollution and to request the Company's assistance as may be necessary.

6 RESOURCES AND PERSONNEL

6.1 The Company should ensure that the master is:

    .1   properly qualified for command;

    .2   fully conversant with the Company's SMS; and

    .3   given the necessary support so that the master's duties can be safely performed.

6.2 The Company should ensure that each ship is manned with qualified, certificated and medically fit seafarers in accordance with national and international requirements.

6.3 The Company should establish procedures to ensure that new personnel and personnel transferred to new assignments related to safety and protection of the environment are given proper familiarisation with their duties. Instructions which are essential to be provided prior to sailing should be identified, documented and given.

6.4 The Company should ensure that all personnel involved in the Company's SMS have an adequate understanding of relevant rules, regulations, codes and guidelines.

6.5 The Company should establish and maintain procedures for identifying any training which may be required in support of the SMS and ensure that such training is provided for all personnel concerned.

6.6 The Company should establish procedures by which the ship's personnel receive relevant information on the SMS in a working language or languages understood by them.

6.7 The Company should ensure that the ship's personnel are able to communicate effectively in the execution of their duties related to the SMS.

7 DEVELOPMENT OF PLANS FOR SHIPBOARD OPERATIONS

The Company should establish procedures for the preparation of plans and instructions for key shipboard operations concerning the safety of the ship and the prevention of pollution. The various tasks involved should be defined and assigned to qualified personnel.

8 EMERGENCY PREPAREDNESS

8.1 The Company should establish procedures to identify, describe and respond to potential emergency shipboard situations.

8.2 The Company should establish programmes for drills and exercises to prepare for emergency actions.

8.3 The SMS should provide for measures ensuring that the Company's organisation can respond at any time to hazards, accidents and emergency situations involving its ships.

9 REPORTS AND ANALYSIS OF NON-CONFORMITIES, ACCIDENTS AND HAZARDOUS OCCURRENCES

9.1 The SMS should include procedures ensuring that non-conformities, accidents and hazardous situations are reported to the Company, investigated and analysed with the objective of improving safety and pollution prevention.

9.2 The Company should establish procedures for the implementation of corrective action.

10 MAINTENANCE OF THE SHIP AND EQUIPMENT

10.1 The Company should establish procedures to ensure that the ship is maintained in conformity with the provisions of the relevant rules and regulations and with any additional requirements which may be established by the Company.

10.2 In meeting these requirements the Company should ensure that:

.1 inspections are held at appropriate intervals;

.2 any non-conformity is reported, with its possible cause, if known;

.3 appropriate corrective action is taken; and

.4 records of these activities are maintained.

10.3 The Company should establish procedures in its SMS to identify equipment and technical systems the sudden operational failure of which may result in hazardous situations. The SMS should provide for specific measures aimed at promoting the reliability of such equipment or systems. These measures should include the regular testing of stand-by arrangements and equipment or technical systems that are not in continuous use.

10.4 The inspections mentioned in 10.2 as well as the measures referred to in 10.3 should be integrated into the ship's operational maintenance routine.

11 DOCUMENTATION

11.1 The Company should establish and maintain procedures to control all documents and data which are relevant to the SMS.

11.2 The Company should ensure that:

.1 valid documents are available at all relevant locations;

.2 changes to documents are reviewed and approved by authorised personnel; and

.3 obsolete documents are promptly removed.

11.3 The documents used to describe and implement the SMS may be referred to as the Safety Management Manual. Documentation should be kept in a form that the Company considers most effective. Each ship should carry on board all documentation relevant to that ship.

12 COMPANY VERIFICATION, REVIEW AND EVALUATION

12.1 The Company should carry out internal safety audits to verify whether safety and pollution-prevention activities comply with the SMS.

12.2 The Company should periodically evaluate the efficiency of and, when needed, review the SMS in accordance with procedures established by the Company.

12.3 The audits and possible corrective actions should be carried out in accordance with documented procedures.

12.4 Personnel carrying out audits should be independent of the areas being audited unless this is impracticable due to the size and the nature of the Company.

12.5 The results of the audits and reviews should be brought to the attention of all personnel having responsibility in the area involved.

12.6 The management personnel responsible for the area involved should take timely corrective action on deficiencies found.

13 CERTIFICATION, VERIFICATION AND CONTROL

13.1 The ship should be operated by a Company which is issued a document of compliance relevant to that ship.

13.2 A document of compliance should be issued for every Company complying with the requirements of the ISM Code by the Administration, by an organisation recognised by the Administration or by the Government of the country, acting on behalf of the Administration in which the Company has chosen to conduct its business. This document should be accepted as evidence that the Company is capable of complying with the requirements of the Code.

13.3 A copy of such a document should be placed on board in order that the master, if so asked, may produce it for the verification of the Administration or organisations recognised by it.

13.4 A certificate, called a Safety Management Certificate, should be issued to a ship by the Administration or organisation recognised by the Administration. The Administration should, when issuing the certificate, verify that the Company and its shipboard management operate in accordance with the approved SMS.

13.5 The Administration or an organisation recognised by the Administration should periodically verify the proper functioning of the ship's SMS as approved.

ANNEX 2: GUIDANCE ON DEVELOPING A SAFETY MANAGEMENT SYSTEM

1. Introduction

It has already been stated that the human element plays some part in virtually all accidents. While the operational responsibility lies with the master, the overall responsibility for the safe operation of the ship rests with the company. Casualty investigations, including Formal Investigations, have shown that good management practice is not always followed. These notes are not a substitute for reading the Code and other useful reference material but are intended to guide and suggest good practice on the development of a Safety Management System which meets the requirements of the Code. It is recognised that not all companies are the same and significant differences will exist between the operation of vessels of different types. Therefore these notes should not be considered as exhaustive.

2. A Safety Management System (SMS)

Meeting the requirements of the ISM Code requires a company to:

- Establish a safety and environmental policy,
- Provide for safe practices,
- Identify risks and establish suitable safeguards,
- Document its management procedures,
- Ensure compliance with relevant rules, regulations and take account of relevant guidelines etc.,
- Define clear lines of responsibility and communication,
- Designate a person ashore responsible for monitoring the safety and pollution prevention aspects of the operation of each ship,
- Provide adequate resources, including suitably qualified and medically fit personnel,
- Provide instructions for shipboard operations and emergency situation,
- Maintain the ship and equipment,
- Provide relevant and current documentation,
- Carry out internal audits and review the SMS.

3. The Designated Person

As already mentioned the Designated Person's (DP) role should not be undervalued. The DP must actively ensure that the ships are properly and responsibly operated and to this end should maintain close contact with Masters and Officers. They should visit the ships at regularly intervals. They should monitor internal audits, corrective actions, safety, accident and casualty reports and the general efficiency of the Safety Management System.

4. Shipboard Instructions and Procedures

4.1 In developing instructions for shipboard operations a suggested outline of the contents which should be included is given below. It is acknowledged that every company and ship is different and the actual contents will vary and change with time. Every ship should carry shipboard instructions, which should contain the following statement:

> "Nothing in these instructions removes from the master his authority to take any steps and issue any orders, whether or not they are in accordance with the instructions, which he considers are necessary for the preservation of life, the safety of the ship or the prevention of pollution".

4.1.1 General

    .1   Documented Company Safety and Environmental Policy and the importance of safety and its relationship to efficient commercial operation.

.2 Company Structure (organogram) which illustrates the lines of communication and the responsibilities within the company and onboard the ship. Identification of the Designated Person and showing his direct access to the highest level of management.

.3 Written statements of authority and responsibility and in particular for the master giving him overriding authority to make decisions with respect to safety and pollution prevention and to request the company's assistance as may be necessary.

.4 Responsibilities of senior officers, duties of other officers, safety officers, safety representatives, petty officers and ratings. Master's and Senior Officers' Standing Orders.

.5 Fitness for duty: Fatigue, drug and alcohol policy.

.6 Action to take if a key crew member, including the master, dies or becomes incapacitated.

.7 Reporting procedures, including internal onboard, from the ship to the company and to others, such as for reporting casualties, accidents and dangerous incidents. (e.g. MCA, MAIB, classification society, insurance company etc.).

.8 Training: Means of identifying training needs, onboard training including drills and external training courses ashore.

.9 Discipline: Application of Code of Conduct for the Merchant Navy, Company policy and grievance procedures.

.10 Procedures for Document Control: How to keep the documents up to date and ways of suggesting improvements and amendments. The system should not be considered as static but continually developing and improving.

.11 Welfare of those onboard: Health, hygiene and safety (e.g. making reference to the Code of Safe Working Practice).

.12 Medical arrangements: Designation of responsible officers, location and custody of medical equipment including First-Aid kits and Ship Captain's Medical Guide. Action in cases beyond the scope of ship-board treatment.

4.1.2 Notes

.1 Reference should be made in appropriate places to legislation, Merchant Shipping Notices, Marine Guidance Notes, Marine Information Notes and Code of Safe Working Practice and other relevant Codes and documents.

.2 The information given is for guidance but ultimately it is the responsibility of the company to develop a system which best suits its needs and those of the Code.

.3 It is recognised that frequent crew changes can influence ship-board organisation. Where ships have multiple crews, all masters must be fully conversant with one standard Safety Management System.

.4 The relevant Safety Management Documents should be available and accessible for all persons who may need to use them. e.g. a set on the bridge, in the engine room and in the hotel department.

.5 Check-lists can be useful to assist routine checks, e.g. prior to sailing, maintenance etc.

4.2 Shipboard Operation: General

.1   Master's and Senior Officers' Standing Orders.

.2   Watch-keeping at sea and in port, including anchor watches. (Refer to STCW as applicable).

.3   Harbour stations: Mooring and Anchoring.

.4   Fire and security patrols and surveillance.

.5   Ship-board maintenance: scheduled maintenance of equipment, consideration being given to "critical systems". On-board repairs, requesting shore assistance for repairs. Defect reporting: procedures for reporting, dealing with and ensuring that defects are rectified. Checks and maintenance of fire-fighting, life saving equipment and emergency lockers.

.6   Maintaining records: The location and persons responsible for keeping relevant records, including e.g. deck, engine, official log books, charts and nautical publications, Merchant Shipping Notices, Marine Guidance Notes, Marine Information Notes, Notices to Mariners and other official publications. Lists of approved berths, technical records and reports, instruction manuals for on-board equipment; stability book, draught records, compass error book, manoeuvring data, shipboard oil pollution and emergency plan, oil record book, statutory and classification certificates etc.

.7   Passenger Control: Embarkation and disembarkation arrangements including the boarding card procedures. Disembarkation information, including information relating to emergency situations, vandalism, alcohol abuse, restraint of passengers in extreme cases, exclusion of unauthorised persons from vehicle decks, ensuring emergency exists, passageways, escapes, fire doors, access to emergency equipment are kept clear at all times.

.8   Inspections by master and senior officers. Routine testing of equipment.

.9   Arrangements and conditions relating to Statutory and Classification Certificates.

.10   Prevention of pollution: Reference to the shipboard oil pollution emergency plan.

.11   Use of pilots and tugs.

.12   Requirements relating to watertight doors.

.13   Requirements relating to bow, stern and other openings in the ship's hull structure.

.14   Safety Committee meetings: Minuted and circulated/posted up.

.15   Onboard internal audits: At specified intervals, identify any non-conformities, take appropriate timely corrective actions.

.16   Onboard review: At specified intervals, evaluate the efficiency of the SMS and bring to the attention of relevant personnel.

4.3 Shipboard Operations: In Port

.1   Embarkation and disembarkation arrangements, boarding card systems, traffic control.

.2 Responsibility for acceptance of cargo. Checking the suitability of vehicles for shipment, securing cargo, dangerous goods, liaison with shore, stowage plans. Continuous monitoring of ship's stability and trim. Operation of loading ramps, moveable decks and other cargo gear. Operation of fork-lift and loading/unloading tractor vehicles. Weight limitations and permissible deck loadings. Precautions against pilferage. Ventilation of vehicle decks and other cargo spaces.

.3 Harbour watches and security patrols. In-port maintenance including procedures to follow when the ship is temporarily immobilised. Liaison with Port Authority and observance of Harbour Byelaws.

.4 Bunkering and storing.

.5 Cargo Operations: preparations, procedures for loading and discharge of tankers (including inert gas systems), gas carriers, bulk carriers and other special ship types as well as general cargo vessels. (refer to the relevant Codes and Port Authority requirements).

.6 Special arrangements during lay-up or refit periods.

.7 Gas freeing of tanks and enclosed spaces.

.8 Hot work and other special hazardous work procedures.

4.4 Preparing For Sea

Note: It is strongly recommended that check lists are drawn up, appropriate to the ship and service, for each officer responsible for various aspects of this section: Completion of these should be recorded in the appropriate log books for each and every voyage.

.1 Verification of passenger numbers.

.2 Reading and recording draughts.

.3 Assessment of Stability. What to do when calculated and observed figures differ.

.4 Checking the securing of vehicles and other cargo.

.5 Checking for leakages from cargo pipelines and manifolds.

.6 Securing hatches and other openings in the hull.

.7 Closing of watertight doors.

.8 Testing of main engines, steering gear, navigation and communications equipment.

.9 Instructions on Bridge/Engine room controls.

.10 Assessment of actual and expected weather and sea state, using both official forecasts and own observations.

.11 Plan of passage made and checked.

.12 Crew on board, at stations and fit for duty.

.13 Report to Master by each responsible officer.

.14 Assessment by Master of readiness to sail. To ensure all statutory and company requirements are complied with. Master to evaluate any reported deficiencies and either satisfy himself that they are acceptable or require them to be rectified before departure.

.15 Documentation of sailing condition.

.16 Clearance.

.17 Safety Broadcasts to passengers.

.18 Rounds of passenger, vehicle and other decks on clearing the berth.

4.5 Shipboard Operations: At Sea

.1 Watchkeeping requirements in general; Bridge, Engine Room and Radio. Masters and Chief Engineers standing orders.

.2 Navigation: Position monitoring. Use of navigational and visual observations. Maintaining dead reckoning. Checks of radio navigation aids and compass by visual observation.

.3 Look-out: Masters Standing Orders and company requirements. Observance of the Collision Regulations and other requirements. Reference to STCW requirements, rest periods etc. Special requirements in fog or bad weather.

.4 Monitoring of machinery and other equipment. Keeping records and logs Cleanliness of machinery spaces. Special requirements when watertight doors are shut. Monitoring the condition of cargo and inert gas systems.

.5 Radio communications including use of VHF.

.6 Fire and safety patrols and surveillance.

.7 Upkeep of deck, engine and radio logs. Movement recording.

.8 Maintaining officers' familiarity with manoeuvring and other data.

.9 Passenger information broadcasts.

.10 Internal communication systems and procedures.

4.6 Emergencies And Contingencies

Contingency planning, drills and musters should cover at least:

.1 General Emergency Procedures, Signals and Organisation with cross-referencing to training manuals.

.2 Fire: Prevention, alarms, first-aid fire-fighting. Fire parties.

.3 Collision; Grounding; Damage Control.

.4 Man Overboard.

.5 Action in the event of the failure of essential equipment. (e.g. main or auxiliary engines, steering).

.6   Obtaining assistance and assisting other vessels or persons. (e.g. towage etc.).

.7   Passenger control in emergency and extreme weather situations.

.8   Communications; within the ship, ship to ship and ship to shore.

.9   Pollution: Large and small oil spills, loss of dangerous goods and other cargo.

References:

The ISM Code embraces aspects of most current conventions and regulations. The following list of documents, which is not exhaustive, gives references which will be of assistance in developing a SMS:

- International Safety Management Code (ISM Code) IMO-186E

- Ship Safety and Pollution Prevention IMO-594E

- Latest consolidated edition of The International Convention for the Safety of Life at Sea, 1974 (SOLAS '74) (and any additional amendments)

- Latest consolidated edition of the International Convention for the Prevention of Pollution from Ships, 1973 and the Protocol of 1978 (MARPOL 73/78) (and any additional amendments)

- STCW 78 (as amended by STCW 95)

- Convention on the International Regulations for Preventing Collisions at Sea, 1972 (as amended)

- Relevant Statutory Instruments

- Merchant Shipping Notices, Marine Guidance Notes and Marine Information Notes, particularly those dealing with:
  Codes of Practice
  Training
  Operational aspects
  Pollution prevention
  Health and Safety issues

- MCA Instructions for the guidance of surveyors (including those for the ISM Code, when published).

- Codes of Practice (e.g. Code of Safe Working Practices for Merchant Seamen, Codes of Practice related to stowage of Cargo, International Safety Guide for Oil Tankers and Terminals (ISGOTT) etc.).

- ICS/ISF Guidelines on the application of the IMO International Safety Management Code.

- ICS Shipping and the Environment A Code of Practice.

MSC/Circ.762
MEPC/Circ.312

ANNEX

GUIDANCE TO COMPANIES OPERATING MULTI-FLAGGED FLEETS AND SUPPLEMENTARY GUIDELINES TO ADMINISTRATIONS

Purpose

1.   To give guidance to companies operating multi-flagged fleets and to give supplementary guidelines to Administrations. To ensure that all Administrations concerned can be satisfied and have faith that the DOC has been issued fully in accordance with resolution A.788(19).

2.   The Assembly, at its nineteenth session, adopted resolution A.788(19) - "Guidelines for Administrations on the implementation of the ISM Code". These guidelines are generally accepted as being a good basis on which Administrations can build as experience is gained in implementing the Code. The same resolution requests Administrations to review the Guidelines in the light of such experience.

3.   Experience to date has highlighted that the Guidelines referred to in paragraph 2 provide no guidance as to how companies operating multi-flagged fleets are to be treated. The absence of such guidance is leading to confusion amongst all sectors of the industry which under certain circumstances may lead to unnecessary duplication of work if not properly addressed, will diminish the impact of the ISM Code on the shipping industry.

4.   The Maritime Safety Committee and the Marine Environment Protective Committee, considering the matter at their sixty-sixth and thirty-eighth sessions respectively, agreed on the following supplementary guidance to be followed by companies and Administrations, as appropriate.

Guidance for companies operating multi-flagged fleets

5.   To facilitate the auditing and certification process companies should approach the relevant flag Administrations, proposing a plan of action and requesting agreement by all parties. This plan should clearly state which entity (see paragraph 8) is to conduct which part of the process.

6.   This approach by companies should be taken at least 12 months prior to the mandatory application date for the particular ship type or types involved.

Supplementary Guidelines to Administrations on auditing and certification of companies operating multi-flagged fleets

7.   Administrations approached by a company operating a multi-flagged fleet should enter into a positive dialogue with other involved Administrations in order to facilitate the auditing and certification process and to avoid unnecessary duplication of work. Relevant agreements may be reached with other involved Administrations for this purpose.

8.   In this respect Administrations should bear in mind that the provision of SOLAS regulation IX/4.1 allows for the following entities to issue DOCs:

- the Administration itself;
- a recognised organisation authorised by the Administration; or
- at the request of the Administration, by another Contracting Government.

9.   The need for establishing a clear link between the shore-based part of the Safety Management System of the company and the shipboard parts should be clearly recognised.

MARINE GUIDANCE NOTE

MGN 71 (M)

Maritime and Coastguard Agency

Musters, drills, on-board training and instructions, and Decision Support Systems

Notice to Owners, Masters, Officers and Ratings

This Note Replaces Marine Guidance Note MGN 17 (M) and should be read in association with MGN 5 and MGN 6.

Summary

This note and annex provides guidance to the relevant requirements in the Regulations listed in paragraph 1 in respect of:

1.   muster lists, the holding of musters and drills and the provision of on-board training and instruction in the use of fire and life-saving appliances, and the provision of a Decision Support System to Masters of certain passenger ships;

2.   the provision of training manuals, and for the manning of survival craft and handling of launching arrangements; and

3.   the closing of openings in the hull and in watertight bulkheads.

1.   The statutory requirements primarily associated with the recommendations and guidance in the Annex to this Notice are prescribed in the following Regulations:

(a) The Merchant Shipping (Musters Training and Decision Support Systems) Regulations 1999 (SI.1999 No.2722) which contains requirements in respect of muster lists, the holding of musters and drills and the provision of on-board training and instruction in the use of fire and lifesaving appliances, and the provision of a Decision Support System to Masters of certain passenger ships;

(b) The Merchant Shipping (Life-Saving Appliances for Ships Other Than Ships of Classes III to VI(A)) Regulations 1999 (SI.1999 No.2721), and the Merchant Shipping (Life-saving Appliances for Passenger Ships of Classes III to VI(A))

Regulations 1999 (SI.1999 No.2723), which contain requirements in respect of the provision of training manuals, and for the manning of survival craft and handling of launching arrangements; and

(c) The Merchant Shipping (Passenger Ship Construction: Ships of Classes I, II and II(A)) Regulations 1998 (SI.1998 No.2514) which contain requirements in respect of the closing of openings in the hull and in watertight bulkheads.

2.   The Regulations referred to in subparagraphs 1(a) and (b) above implement the 1983 and 1988 and 1996 Amendments to Chapter III of the International Convention for the Safety of Life at Sea 1974. One of the principal objectives of the 1983 Amendments to the Convention was to prescribe minimum standards of training and instruction, in particular on-board training in the use of ship's fire appliances, ship's life-saving

appliances including launching and embarkation equipment, in methods of survival and in the use of personal protective equipment. An essential part of such training and instruction involves participation in periodic practice musters and drills. The 1996 Amendment introduced the requirement for Decision Support Systems for Masters of certain passenger ships.

3.   The purpose of this Note and its Annex is to draw attention to relevant requirements in the Regulations listed in paragraph 1 and to specify how such requirements should be met.

MSPP2c
Maritime and Coastguard Agency
Spring Place
105 Commercial Road
Southampton
S015 1EG

Tel: 01703 329184
Fax: 01703 329204

October 1999

MS 050/005/0005

© Crown Copyright 1999

An executive agency of the Department of the Environment, Transport and the Regions

ANNEX

1   Application

1.1   Except where otherwise specified the contents of this Annex are addressed to ships of Classes I, II, II(A), III, VII, VII(A), VII(T), VIII, VIII(T), VIII(A), VIII(A)(T) and IX and to ships of Class XI engaged on international voyages.

2   Muster Lists

2.1   The requirements relating to muster lists apply to ships engaged on international voyages and to passenger ships of Classes II(A) and III. The Master is responsible for compiling the muster list, keeping it up to date and ensuring that copies are exhibited in conspicuous places throughout the ship, including the navigating bridge, engineroom and crew accommodation. The format of muster lists for ships of Classes I, II, II(A) and III must be approved by the Maritime and Coastguard Agency (MCA).

2.2   In ships with significant numbers of non-English speaking crew members, the muster list should include translations into the appropriate language or languages.

2.3   The muster list must contain details of the general emergency alarm and other emergency signals and the action to be taken by the crew and passengers in respect of the former, and by the crew in respect of the latter. Where appropriate, communication equipment, channels and reporting chain to be used during an abandonment or other emergency should be specified. The means by which the order to abandon ship is to be given must also be included.

2.4   The muster list must show the duties to be carried out by each member of the ship's complement in an emergency. Such duties include the preparation, swinging out or deploying of survival craft and other life-saving appliances, the closing of watertight and fire doors, and all other openings such as skylights, portholes and side scuttles and any openings in the hull. Duties in connection with fire-fighting, the use of communication equipment and the equipping of survival craft must also be shown.

2.5   Where passengers are carried duties include warning and assembling passengers, controlling their movement, seeing that they are suitably clad and wearing their lifejackets correctly or, where appropriate, distributing and assisting with the donning of lifejackets, and, where carried, taking a supply of blankets to the survival craft.

2.6   In assigning crew members to assist passengers in emergency situations on ships of Classes I, II, II(A) and III masters should ensure that all such personnel have received instruction in crowd management.

2.7   As far as practicable each individual should only be allocated one duty, or series of duties related to one emergency party. On passenger ships key persons who would be last to abandon ship should not be allocated to those survival craft which are expected to be the first to be launched.

2.8　When the muster list is compiled consideration should be given to the eventuality of key persons being unable to carry out their emergency duties through injury or for some other reason, and provision made for substitutes. This provision must be shown on the muster list and may be a detailed list or in the form of a general statement such as "Should key persons become disabled, those next in line, as appropriate, should take their place". When allocating substitutes care should be exercised to ensure that emergency parties are not left without a leader or seriously undermanned.

2.9　The survival craft or launching station to which each crew member is assigned should be shown on the muster list.

2.10　In assigning crew members to man survival craft and handle launching appliances on ships engaged on international voyages and on passenger ships of Classes II(A) and III, the Master should take account of Merchant Shipping Notice MSN 1682 (M).

2.11　A deck officer or certificated person must be placed in charge of each survival craft to be used and a deck officer or certificated person must be assigned as second-in-command of a lifeboat. In ships of Classes II, II(A) and III a person practiced in the handling and operation of liferafts may be placed in charge of a liferaft in lieu of a deck officer or certificated person. The person in charge of the survival craft shall have a list of the survival craft crew and shall see that the crew under his command are acquainted with their duties. In lifeboats the second-in-command shall also have a list of the lifeboat crew.

2.12　A motor lifeboat must have a person assigned to it who is capable of operating the engine and carrying out minor adjustments. This person may be the coxswain if it is possible to operate the engine and steer the lifeboat from one position. A lifeboat with a radio installation and each survival craft in which are placed emergency position-indicating radio beacons (EPIRBs), radar transponders (SARTs), or two-way radio-telephone sets is required to have a person assigned to it who is capable of operating such equipment.

2.13　The muster list must show the name or rank of the officers whose duty is to ensure that the life-saving and fire-fighting appliances are maintained in such condition as to be always ready for use.

2.14　In passenger ships, the location of the passenger assembly or muster station (as appropriate) must be indicated in the muster list. As far as practicable, public rooms will be allocated as assembly or muster station (as appropriate) in order that passengers are protected from the elements prior to their departure for the survival craft if the ship has to be abandoned.

2.15　The master shall ensure the equitable distribution of persons referred to in paragraph 2.6, 2.10 and 2.11 among the ship's survival craft.

3　Emergency Instructions

3.1　In ships engaged on international voyages and in passenger ships of Classes II(A) and III, each crew member must be provided with clear instructions to be followed in the event of an emergency, eg in the form of a card showing the assembly or muster station (as appropriate) station, emergency duty and the lifeboat or liferaft to which he is allocated. In ships with significant numbers of non-English speaking crew members emergency instructions should be provided in the appropriate language or languages. The card or other means should describe the general emergency alarm signal and any other signals to be used in an emergency and the action, if any, to be taken on hearing such signals. The means by which the order to abandon ship is to be given should also be included.

3.2　Emergency instructions, illustrated where possible, must be displayed in each passenger cabin, in passenger assembly or muster station (as appropriate) stations and in other passenger spaces. Such instructions, in English and in any other language appropriate to the principal nationalities carried on the route on which the ship is operating, are to inform passengers of their assembly or muster station (as appropriate) stations, essential actions they should take on hearing the general emergency alarm signal and any other signal requiring action on their part, and the method of donning lifejackets. The location of lifejackets should be included in these instructions. Safety information to be provided to passengers is detailed in Merchant Shipping Notices M.1386 (to be replaced by MGN 73) and M.1409 (to be replaced by MGN 74).

4　Emergency Signals

4.1　The general emergency alarm signal is the signal for summoning the crew and passengers, if any, to their assembly or muster station (as appropriate) stations and for initiating the actions shown in the muster list. This signal consists of seven or more short blasts followed by one long blast sounded on the ship's whistle or siren and on a bell, klaxon or similar warning system on ships required to be provided with such systems.

4.2   On a cargo ship with a fire alarm system which can be manually activated from locations within the accommodation or where a system such as a fire or smoke detection system automatically activates alarms throughout the ship, the signal made by such means may be used to summon the crew to their muster stations. Such alarm signal should be accompanied by the general emergency alarm signal sounded on the whistle or siren.

4.3   Signals for incidents not requiring a muster of the passengers or of the whole crew, or for dealing with a minor incident, are at the Master's discretion.

4.4   On a cargo ship a signal may be allocated to summon the crew to survival craft embarkation stations only, for the purpose of a drill or mustering the crew at the survival craft embarkation stations during an emergency.

4.5   The means by which the order to abandon ship is given is at the Master's discretion and may be by a signal or by word of mouth, but arrangements should be such that everyone on board including those in emergency parties in remote locations will receive it.

4.6   All signals must be described in the muster list, in the crew emergency instructions and, as appropriate, in the emergency instructions for passengers.

4.7   The relevant signals referred to in this section should be used when musters and drills are to be conducted. All persons on board should be notified beforehand that a practice muster or drill is about to be held.

5   Musters and Drills - General

5.1   An abandon ship drill consists of a muster of the crew (and of passengers, if appropriate) at the stations referred to in the muster list, and a muster and drill at survival craft stations. Where practicable, passengers on Class I passenger ships should be strongly

encouraged to attend abandon ship drills. It is recommended that a fire drill be held simultaneously with the first stage of the abandon ship drill. Drills for emergencies other than fire, eg collision, damage control, grounding, cargo or bunker spillage, rescue of personnel from dangerous spaces, or medical treatment, may be conducted in lieu of or in addition to a fire drill, provided each crew member participates in at least one fire drill each month. Whether a fire or other emergency drill is to be conducted, it may be found useful on occasions to discuss beforehand, with those taking a direct part in the drill, the object and execution of the drill in order that those taking part can derive the maximum benefit from the drill. When planning procedures and associated drills dealing with rescue of personnel from dangerous spaces, account should be taken of Chapters 16 and 17 of the Code of Safe Working Practices for Merchant Seamen, 1998 Edition.

5.2   Each crew member must participate in at least one abandon ship drill and one fire drill every month. These drills must be held within 24 hours of leaving port if more than 25% of the crew have not taken part in drills on board the ship in the previous month. If circumstances are such that it is not practical to hold full drills within the 24 hours then musters should be held within this period and instructions given to crew members on their emergency duties and on abandon ship procedures, but in the case of Ro-Ro passenger ferries these instructions should be given before any passenger carrying voyage is commenced. Full drills should be held as soon as circumstances permit. In addition, in ships of Classes I, II, II(A) and III, an abandon ship drill and a fire drill must be held weekly and as many of the crew as practicable should take part in these drills which should be so arranged that each crew member participates in at least one abandon ship drill and one fire drill every month.

5.3   On any ship carrying passengers where the passengers are scheduled to be on board for more than 24 hours, a muster of the passengers must take place within 24 hours of their embarkation. Passengers must be given instruction in how to don their lifejackets and the action to take on hearing the general emergency alarm signal. If only a small number of passengers embark after the muster has been held, it will be sufficient, instead of holding another, to draw the attention of these passengers to the emergency instructions referred to in paragraph 3.2. Similarly, on ships of Classes other than the above carrying passengers, if a muster of the passengers is not held on departure, their attention must be drawn to the emergency instructions referred to in paragraph 3.2. This can be done by means of a broadcast on the ship's public address system or by direct oral announcement.

5.4   It should be drawn to the attention of the passengers that the general emergency alarm signal is for the purpose of summoning them to their assembly or muster station (as appropriate) stations and is not a signal to abandon ship. The means by which the order to abandon ship will be given should be explained. The importance of being properly clad, of proceeding to their assembly or muster station (as appropriate) station in an orderly fashion, and of following instructions at all times should be emphasised. Where appropriate they should be advised to which type of survival craft they have been allocated, and how they will be embarked. They should be advised that only as a last resort will it be necessary to jump into the water. They should be informed of the dangers of jumping overboard, particularly from heights in excess of 6 metres and advised that if it should be necessary to jump into the water, the lifejacket must be held down with one hand and the nose protected with the other hand.

5.5   Lifejackets should be worn by passengers and crew when attending musters and drills. Crew members taking part in fire and other emergency drills may remove their lifejackets if these would be a hindrance in the execution of their duties. Where lifejackets are removed, a member of the emergency party concerned should be appointed to be responsible for these lifejackets and to ensure that they will be available for return to the members of an emergency party on completion of their relevant tasks. Where inherently buoyant lifejackets unduly hinder crew members in the execution of their duties, consideration should be given to the provision of inflatable lifejackets, although such lifejackets are not always suitable for use by members of fire hose parties due to the possibility of inadvertent activation of the automatic inflation system. Lifejackets should always be worn by members of survival craft preparation parties and at survival craft musters and drills.

5.6   On passenger ships consideration should be given to the identification of crew members, particularly those whose duties are concerned with passenger control. This can be achieved in a variety of ways, eg by the use of headgear, distinctive marking on lifejackets, loose covers worn over lifejackets, armbands, etc.

5.7   On passenger ships as many key persons as possible should carry two-way portable radios during musters and drills and such radios and any fixed two-way communication systems should be used for communications between the bridge, emergency control stations, assembly or muster station (as appropriate) and embarkation stations, especially internal Marine Evacuation System (MES) embarkation stations. Where key persons do not have a two-way portable radio on permanent issue there should be arrangements whereby radios can be readily obtained at the outset of a drill or actual emergency. Where portable loud hailers are carried these should be used where appropriate for communicating or for simulating communicating with passengers at assembly or muster station (as appropriate) and embarkation stations. The arrangements for communication should be as recorded in muster lists and, where applicable, training manuals.

6   Abandon Ship Drills

6.1   The commencement of an abandon ship drill is announced by the general emergency alarm signal. Crew and passengers, if any, should proceed to their assembly or muster station (as appropriate) stations. Crew members allocated to the handling of passengers should as appropriate clear or simulate the clearing of accommodation not used for the mustering of passengers, marshall passengers taking part in the drill and control the flow of passengers on the stairways, in passages and doorways and guide them towards their assembly or muster station (as appropriate) stations. At the assembly or muster station (as appropriate) stations they should ensure that passengers have donned their lifejackets correctly, or give instruction in donning as appropriate, and that child lifejackets are allocated to persons of less than 32 Kg. Passengers should be advised on the matters referred to in paragraph 5.4. Where a proportion of the survival craft consists of throwover liferafts boarded by means of ship's side ladders provision should be made for allocating only able bodied passengers to these liferafts. It should also be determined that crew members know how the order to abandon ship will be announced, that they are suitably dressed and that their lifejackets have been donned correctly.

7 Fire and other Emergency Drills

7.1 A fire or other emergency drill shall as far as practicable be conducted as if it were an actual emergency.

7.2 A fire or other emergency drill should be held simultaneously with the first stage of the abandon ship drill.

7.3 For the purpose of a fire drill an outbreak of fire should be assumed to have occurred in some part of the ship and fire control measures simulated as appropriate. The complete co-operation of the personnel of all departments is essential in fire fighting. The type and position of the supposed fire should be varied from time to time and can include:

(1) Cargo fires in holds or other spaces;

(2) Fires involving oil, gas or chemical cargoes as appropriate;

(3) Fires in engine, pump or boiler rooms;

(4) Fires in crew or passenger accommodation; and

(5) Fires in galleys due to burning oil or cooking fats.

7.4 The engine room staff should ensure that the fire pumps in the machinery spaces are prepared for operation, started, and that full water pressure is on the fire mains. Where there is an emergency fire pump situated outside the machinery space, this pump should be started up as indicated below. The fire party or parties at the scene of the assumed fire should lay out hoses and where practicable water should be played through them, the water being supplied first from the machinery space pump and then from the emergency pump only, with the machinery space isolating valve closed. A number of portable fire extinguishers should be available and members of the fire party should be instructed in the use of the type of fire extinguisher for a particular type of fire.

7.5 The crew should be exercised as appropriate in the closing of openings, ie side scuttles, deadlights, doors, ventilating shafts, fire doors, the annular space around the funnel, etc both to reduce the supply of air to a fire and

isolate it from other parts of the ship, especially stairways and lift shafts. As many of the crew as possible and particularly the officers should be made familiar with the position of remote controls for ventilation fans, oil fuel pumps and oil tank valves and be instructed in the method of operation thereof.

7.6 Fixed installations for extinguishing fire, such as Halon, CO_2, foam, or water spray in the machinery spaces, CO_2, inert gas, steam or drencher systems in the cargo spaces, and sprinkler systems in passenger accommodation together with fire alarm and detection systems should be tested with as much realism as practicable. The fire party should also be exercised in the use of the breathing apparatus and protective clothing and such emergency appliances as axes and safety lamps, which should be brought out, checked and deployed by appointed members of the party at all fire drills. Where the number of sets of breathing apparatus permits, it is recommended that persons using them should practice in pairs.

7.7 It is important that members of the crew who are not allocated to fire parties are familiar with the use of and can identify the types of fire extinguisher they will encounter in the accommodation and in their work areas. Such crew members should be instructed in the use of the type of extinguisher appropriate to the kind of fire, eg those discharging water, foam, dry powder, CO_2, etc.

7.8 At each fire drill at least one extinguisher should be discharged by a different crew member in order that both crew members in fire parties and other crew members gain experience in using fire extinguishers. Crew members should also be familiar with the location and means of activating the fire alarms in the accommodation and in their working areas. It is also important that all crew members and particularly those whose place of work is in a machinery space are familiar with the escape routes from any part of the ship they are likely to be in when on or off duty. Such familiarity should enable escape to be made in darkness or through smoke and should include familiarity with the location and the means of opening any emergency escape windows or hatches.

7.9 All fire protection systems and appliances should at all times be in good order and available for immediate use during the voyage and in port. Compressed air bottles of breathing apparatus and fire extinguishers should be refilled after any drill. Where refilling facilities are not available on board additional equipment may be carried to facilitate training. Discharged equipment should be clearly marked and stored for refilling when in port. Equipment dedicated for training purposes should be marked 'for training purposes only'.

7.10   Participation in fire drills may not necessarily imply direct involvement with fighting a fire and may include back-up to fire parties, being a member of the first aid party or controlling passengers at their assembly or muster station (as appropriate) stations while the fire fighting part of the drill is being undertaken. On the other hand, on cargo ships with small crews it will usually be necessary for every member of the crew to be familiar with all aspects of fire-fighting and the use of all the fire-fighting equipment provided on board the ship.

7.11   Instruction should cover fire prevention, particularly in galleys, machinery spaces, cargo compartments, pumprooms and accommodation spaces. On-board instruction in fire-fighting is supplementary to training available at firefighting courses ashore and is primarily concerned with the particular equipment available on board and the nature of on-board fire hazards.

7.12   To ensure the ready availability of fire protection systems and appliances periodic checks should be performed. The following checklist may be used as guidance for this purpose.

7.12.1   Monthly testing and inspection should be carried out to ensure that:

(1)   all firemans outfits, fire extinguishers, fire hydrants, hose and nozzles are in place and in serviceable condition;

(2)   all escape routes including stairways and corridors are free of obstructions and properly maintained;

(3)   public address system and ship's alarms are serviceable;

(4)   all fixed fire fighting installation valves are set in the correct operational position;

(5)   dry pipe sprinkler systems are pressurised, where appropriate, and gauges indicate correctly;

(6)   sprinkler system pressure tank water levels are correct as indicated by glass gauges;

(7)   all sprinkler system pumps operate automatically on pressure loss in the systems;

(8)   all fire pumps are operational; and

(9)   all fixed gas fire extinguishing installations are free from leakage.

7.12.2   Quarterly testing and inspection should be carried out to ensure that:

(1)   all fire extinguishers are at correct pressure and are not due for servicing;

(2)   all automatic alarms for sprinkler systems activate using the section test valves;

(3)   the international shore connection is serviceable;

(4)   fire fighting equipment lockers contain their full inventory and the equipment they contain is in serviceable condition; and

(5)   all fire doors, fire dampers and closing devices can be operated locally.

7.12.3   Annual testing and inspection should be carried out to ensure that:

(1)   all fire doors, and ventilation dampers where appropriate, operate remotely;

(2)   where practicable all aqueous foam and water spray fixed fire fighting installations operate correctly;

(3)   all accessible components of fixed fire fighting systems, typically nozzles, are free from damage or obstruction on visual inspection;

(4)   all fire pumps, including sprinkler system pumps, develop correct pressures and flow rates;

(5)   all hydrants operate;

(6)   all antifreeze solutions are correctly maintained and cross connection between

fire main and sprinkler system operates correctly; and

(7) fixed fire detection systems operate correctly, according to manufacturers test instructions.

7.13 Fire or other emergency drills should be followed by the second stage of the abandon ship drill ie the muster and drill at the survival craft stations. This stage of the abandon ship drill should be announced by the abandon ship signal or by the particular means by which abandon ship is announced, or by a signal used for the purpose of summoning crew members to their survival craft stations.

8 Drills in Closing of Doors, Side Scuttles and Other Openings

8.1 In passenger ships, drills for practicing the closing of watertight doors, deadlights, scuppers, ash-shutes, rubbish-shutes and other similar devices are required to be carried out to comply with the Merchant Shipping (Passenger Ship Construction: Ships of Classes I, II, and II(A)) Regulations 1998, or the Merchant Shipping (Passenger Ship Construction: Ships of Classes III to VI(A)) Regulations 1998. These Regulations also require inspections, at intervals of not more than 7 days, of watertight doors and mechanisms, indicators and warning devices connected with such doors, valves, the closing of which is necessary to make watertight any compartment below the margin line, and valves, the operation of which is necessary for the efficient operation of damage-control cross-connections.

8.2 In all seagoing ships, with certain exceptions, the Merchant Shipping (Musters Training and Decision Support Systems) Regulations 1999 require practice fire drills to include checking of the operation of watertight doors, in the drill area.

8.3 Masters should familiarise themselves with the Regulations referred to in paragraphs 8.1 and 8.2, particularly in regard to the instruction of crew members in the safe operation of watertight doors and to those watertight doors, side scuttles, deadlights and other devices required to be securely closed before the ship proceeds to sea and to be kept securely closed while the ship is at sea.

Account should also be taken of the contents of Merchant Shipping Notice M.1326 (to be replaced by MGN 35 (M)) on the dangers associated with power operated watertight doors, and of the Instructions for the Guidance of Surveyors (Passenger Ship Construction Classes I, II and II(A)) and (Passenger Ship Construction Classes III to VIA).

9 Survival Craft Muster and Drill

9.1 Crew members other than those who cannot be relieved from their normal duties should muster, wearing lifejackets, at their lifeboat and liferaft stations. The person in charge of each survival craft must have a list of its crew and ensure that they are fully acquainted with their duties. The second-in-command of a lifeboat must also have a list of the lifeboat crew.

9.1.1 On passenger ships, the lifeboats used in the drill should where practicable, include some from each side of the ship and should be distributed as to enable the crews of the other lifeboats to watch the operations. Different groups of lifeboats should be used at successive drills.

9.1.2 In cargo ships provided with totally enclosed lifeboats which are boarded and launched from the stowed position, drills should periodically include the boarding of a lifeboat in its stowed position in order that crew members can become practiced in boarding a boat rapidly, locating a seating position and using the seat belts.

9.1.3 In the case of other totally enclosed lifeboats equipped with seatbelts, crew members should be periodically drilled in using the seatbelts but such lifeboats should not be boarded at the stowed position by the full complement at any one time. When a drill is being carried out inside a totally enclosed lifeboat, crew members should also be made familiar with the launching procedures and made aware of what to expect when the engine and air support and water spray systems, where fitted, are in operation.

9.1.4 Arrangements should always be made to ensure that those crew members who cannot be relieved from their duties to attend a particular drill can be relieved to attend the next drill.

9.2 On passenger ships when the drill is held at sea, a number of lifeboats should, if weather and other circumstances permit and subject to overriding safety constraints, be cleared, swung out, and lowered to embarkation deck level in the case of lifeboats boarded at this position, and side ladders and embarkation arrangements prepared. On cargo ships at least one lifeboat should be lowered when weather and other circumstances permit.

9.3 Each lifeboat and rescue boat engine must be tested by being run ahead and astern for a total period of not less than 3 minutes provided that the engine can be safely run for this period when out of the water and the ambient temperature is above the minimum required for starting the engine. Where lifeboats are fitted with mechanical hand-propelling gear, this gear should be examined and tested ahead and astern.

9.4 Liferaft davits must be swung out and winches operated.

9.5 Emergency lighting for mustering and abandonment must be tested at each such drill.

9.6 In cargo ships provided with lifeboats and throwover liferafts some drills should include preparation for abandonment involving use of liferafts in conjunction with lifeboats. This may include mustering at locations other than those used for embarkation into lifeboats

10 Survival Craft Drills Held in Port

10.1 When a drill is held in port as many as possible of the lifeboats should be cleared, swung out and lowered. Each lifeboat must be launched with its assigned operating crew aboard and manoeuvered in the water once every 3 months during an abandon ship drill. In lifeboats not fitted with engines the crew should be exercised in rowing or in the use of the mechanical hand-propelling gear. Every opportunity should be taken to test the lifeboat disengaging gear where fitted.

10.2 If the berthing arrangements in port and the trading patterns of ships of Classes II, II(A), VIII or VIII(A) make the launching of lifeboats on one side impracticable then launching of lifeboats on that side at 3 monthly intervals need not be carried out. However all such lifeboats must be lowered at least once every 3 months and launched at least annually.

10.3 The launching of lifeboats and rescue boats should normally take place when the ship is alongside or at anchor with little or no tide or current, but if contemplated in circumstances where there is actual or effective headway, such launching must be carried out in accordance with the guidelines in the Annex to Merchant Shipping Notice M. 1218. (to be replaced by MSN 1722 (M + F).

10.4 A free-fall lifeboat may be lowered to the water if launching is impracticable, provided that free-fall launching with the assigned operating crew and manoeuvering in the water is carried out at least once every six months. If it is impracticable to launch within a period of six months, the Owners may apply to the MCA for an extension to twelve months.

11 Rescue Boat and Emergency Boat Drills

11.1 As far as is reasonable and practicable rescue boats where carried, other than those which are also lifeboats, must be launched each month with their rescue boat crews and manoeuvered in the water. The interval between such drills must not exceed 3 months. Where climatic conditions permit, the crew of a rescue boat should wear their immersion suits during such in-water drills. Where possible such drills should include the recovery of an object simulating a person in the water. Emergency boats carried on passenger ships which do not carry rescue boats should be launched at similar intervals and should carry out similar drill procedures.

11.2 In ships of Class I the crews of rescue and emergency boats should be mustered on the first day of the voyage as soon as possible after sailing. The crews should be fully instructed and drilled in their duties and thereafter should be mustered and similarly drilled at intervals of not more than 7 days. Crews should be specifically instructed in the procedure of sending boats away promptly in an emergency and in recovering boats in a seaway, and should be familiar with the signal for mustering at the rescue or emergency boat station.

12 Davit-launched Liferaft On-Board Training

12.1 On-board training in the use of davit-launched liferafts must take place at intervals of not more than 4 months on every ship fitted with such liferafts. Whenever practicable this training includes the inflation and lowering of a liferaft. This liferaft may be a special liferaft intended for training purposes only or an old liferaft retained for training and not part of the ship's life-saving equipment. A special liferaft intended for training purposes only is required to be conspicuously marked and, if intended to be used for boarding when swung out at the embarkation deck, should be serviced at the same intervals as the liferafts forming part of the ship's life-saving equipment.

12.2   In preparing an on-board training programme for davit-launched liferafts the procedures adopted should take full account of the structural arrangements in way of the launching positions. For example it may not be possible to recover an inflated liferaft from an overside position without subjecting it to the risk of damage. Where procedures described in paragraphs 12.3 and 12.5 cannot be safely followed, other arrangements should be made which will enable on-board training of an equivalent standard to be carried out.

12.3   In ships of Classes II and II(A) on regular voyages, the four monthly on-board training in the use of davit-launched liferafts should include an inflation of one of the ship's liferafts. These inflations should take place when in port and where practical the liferaft should be lowered unloaded onto the quay rather than into the water. Training in boarding and using the release hook can be carried out when the liferaft is suspended just clear of the quay. The liferaft should be landed on a tarpaulin or heavy Polythene sheet to prevent any damage to the bottom of the raft. If it is not practical to land the liferaft on the quay, the boarding and use of the release hook can be carried out with the liferaft suspended just clear of the embarkation deck following initial inflation in the overside position. In this case the liferaft need not be lowered over the side but a weight should be attached to the release hook and then lowered to exercise the winch and give crew members practice in the handling of the winch and fall.

12.4   After this training the liferaft used should be sent for servicing. It is recommended that different liferafts be used at successive drills in order to avoid wear on a small number of liferafts.

12.5   In cargo ships and in passenger ships on irregular voyages, eg Class I cruise ships, there should be an inflation of one of the ship's liferafts at one of the four monthly on-board training

sessions in the use of davit-launched liferafts. The training should be carried out as described in paragraph 12.3 and the liferaft serviced as soon as possible after use. On the other two occasions in the twelve month period when the four monthly on-board training is carried out, this can be done using, for example, a practice raft and practice container. If such training is carried out in port, then the procedure described in paragraph 12.3 should be followed. If such training is carried out at sea, means should be provided for suspending and lowering the raft over a deck to provide the opportunity for boarding and handling the release hook.

12.6   Alternatively the procedure for ships engaged on regular voyages can be followed if this is more convenient.

13   On-board Instruction, Training and Training Manuals

13.1   Before being assigned to shipboard duties, all persons employed or engaged on a seagoing ship other than passengers, shall receive appropriate familiarisation training in compliance with Reg VI/1 of the STCW95 Convention. This training is in addition to other shore based training required under the STCW95 Convention. Where thermal protective aids are carried every crew member should be trained in donning the aid while wearing a lifejacket. Crew members who have been allocated an immersion suit should be trained in the donning of the suit and given the opportunity to familiarise themselves with the wearing of the suit.

13.2   Crew members whose emergency duties include the guidance of passengers, and the searching and closing down of passenger spaces should be trained and instructed in these duties. Such training and instruction should cover the matters referred to in 6.1 above, in MGN 5, and should include the use of procedures for reducing or avoiding panic and the giving of clear reassuring orders. The training should be given prior to being assigned such duties on Ro-Ro passenger ships and other passenger ships.

13.3   Crew members allocated specific key tasks for the preparation, launching and handling of lifeboats, rescue boats, liferafts and marine evacuation systems should be trained in these specific tasks. Such training should also be given to a sufficient number of crew members to provide substitutes for the crew members allocated these key tasks in the muster list. The importance of training, particularly in the handling of totally enclosed and partially enclosed motor propelled lifeboats fitted with onload release gear and in certain cases with self-contained air support and water spray systems, cannot be emphasised enough due to the complexity of such equipment. Training given on board is primarily concerned with the particular life-saving equipment carried and is supplementary to shore based training given on personal survival techniques, on proficiency in survival craft and rescue boat, and training-courses organised by individual owners. The training should include ship specific practices such as the normal sequence for preparing and safely deploying evacuation systems, launching lifeboats and liferafts, and all other factors which determine rate of evacuation, and may also cover alternatives to the normal sequence of deployment.

13.4   Where on-board training cannot be given in the use of certain items of life-saving equipment because of practical considerations, on-board instructions in the use of such equipment is required to be given at the same intervals as the drills. Instructions are required to be given in survival procedures including the causes of and first aid treatment for hypothermia, and first aid measures likely to be practiced in a survival craft. Instructions include the operation and use of the ship's liferafts and embarkation arrangements and the use of survival craft and rescue boats in severe weather and sea conditions. Instructions may also include actions to be taken in the event of foreseeable equipment failures.

13.5   The basic information on which these instructions will be based will be found in the ship's life-saving appliances training manual which contains instructions and information on the life-saving appliances carried, personal protective equipment and its location, in addition to information and instructions on survival, hazards of exposure, methods of retrieval and emergency repair of life-saving appliances. Any part of the information to be included in the Training Manual may be provided in the form of audio-visual aids. Information provided in lifesaving appliances training manuals should be compatible with, and may reproduce, relevant shipboard safety emergency plans which are required to be provided in accordance with the International Safety Management Code (SOLAS 1974 Chapter IX; reference should also be made to MSC/Circ.760 "Guidelines for a Structure of an Integrated System of Contingency Planning for Shipboard Emergencies."). (See paragraph 15.6)

13.6   The training manual can be used by the officer or officers whose duty it is to give the relevant instructions and it can also be used as a source of reference and information for every member of the crew. A copy of the training manual should be accessible to every crew member and except in certain ships of less than 500 GRT, a copy must be provided in each messroom and recreation room, or in each cabin.

13.7   In ships with significant numbers of non-English speaking crew members, copies of the full training manual or relevant sections should be provided in the appropriate language or languages.

13.8   The programme of instructions must be so arranged that every subject to be covered, including all parts of the ship's life-saving systems can be treated within a two month period. In order to carry out this programme in cargo ships, the frequency of holding drills may have to be increased beyond that necessary to ensure that every crew member participates in an abandon ship and fire drill every month. Frequent short periods of instruction dealing with a limited number of items will be more effective than long sessions dealing with a considerable amount of subject matter and held say at monthly intervals.

14   Weekly and Monthly Inspection of LSA

14.1   Weekly and monthly inspections as described in paragraph 14.2 and 14.3 must be carried out on all ships to which the Merchant Shipping (Life-Saving Appliances for Ships Other Than Ships of Classes III to VI(A)) Regulations 1999, and the Merchant Shipping (Life-saving Appliances for Passenger Ships of Classes III to VI(A)) Regulations 1999, apply.

14.2   At weekly intervals survival craft, rescue boats and launching appliances must be inspected to ensure that they are ready for immediate use. Rescue boat and lifeboat engines must be run at weekly intervals. The general emergency alarm system must also be tested every week.

14.3   All lifesaving appliances including lifeboat and rescue boat equipment is required to be inspected at monthly intervals. For this purpose the checklist provided in the instructions for onboard maintenance is used. This inspection should include the examination and testing of any fixed radio installations and searchlight equipment, and ensuring that the batteries can be charged from the dynamo when the engine is running.

14.4   In lifeboats with water spray systems, each system should be tested at intervals of not more than 3 months in accordance with the manufacturer's instructions. The system should be flushed through with fresh water after testing with sea water.

15   Decision Support System

15.1   Passenger ships of Classes I, II and II(A) are required to have a decision support system for emergency management on the navigation bridge. It can be printed on paper, or computer based, and must identify all foreseeable emergency situations, establish emergency procedures for each situation, and provide decisive support to the Master.

15.2   Reference should be made to MSC/Circ.760 "Guidelines for a Structure of an Integrated System of Contingency Planning for Shipboard Emergencies".

15.3   The Guidelines noted above are intended to help integrate the various contingency Plans currently required by SOLAS and MARPOL, into a structured and consistent format. The Plans are required be in a uniform structure, be clear and easy to understand.

15.4   The Plans must be available in the working language of the Master, Officers and relevant crew members, and must be appropriately amended if the working language changes.

15.5   Training, drills, and records of such, of the Decision Support System, should be integrated into the overall training regime.

15.6   Copies of MSC/Circ.760 are available from the Marine Information Centre of the MCA:

Tel: 01703 329297
Fax: 01703 329298

16   Records

16.1   The date on which musters, drills and training sessions are held, the type of drill and training held, and the occasions on which lifeboats, rescue boats and davit-launched liferafts, as applicable, are lowered or launched must be entered in the official log book.

16.2   Where a full muster, drill or training session as required by the Merchant Shipping (Musters Training and Decision Support Systems)

Regulations 1999, is not held a record must be made of the relevant circumstances and the extent of any muster, drill or training session held.

Bibliography

The Bridge Procedures Guide – International Chamber of Shipping

Bridge Watchkeeping A Practical Guide – Nautical Institute

Code of Safe Working Practice for Merchant Seaman – HMSO

IAMSAR Manual Volume III – IMO

Maritime Meteorology – M. Cornish and E. Ives

Seamanship Handbook – G. Bonwick

The Ships Compass – G. Grant and J. Klinkert

The Shiphander's Guide – R.W. Rowe

The Shipmaster's Business Companion – M.S. Maclachlan

The Theory and Practice of Seamanship – Danton

Safety of Navigation Implementing SOLAS Chapter V – Maritime and Coastguard Agency

Merchant Shipping Notices – Maritime and Coastguard Agency

www.amver.com – Automated Mutual-assistance Vessel Rescue System

www.imo.org – International Maritime Organisation

www.fire-uk.org/offshore.htm – The Chief Fire Officers Association

www.mcga.gov.uk – Maritime and Coastguard Agency

Environmental – Counter Pollution and Response

HM Coastguard – SAR

www.metoffice.gov.uk – Met Office

www.navcen.uscg.gov – US Coast Guard Navigation Centre

Seamanship Techniques: Shipboard and Marine Operations, Third Edition – D. J. House. Published by Elsevier, 2004. ISBN: 0750663154.